LEARNING TOGETHER

ADVICE AND INSTRUCTIONS ON COMPLETING THESE TESTS

1. These tests are in multiple-choice format and you have to mark your answers on a separate answer sheet.

2. Some questions ask you to mark more than one answer. Read the questions carefully.

3. Use a pencil and draw a line clearly through the middle of the box next to your chosen answer.

4. If you change an answer make sure the change is clear. Use an eraser to rub out the wrong answer.

5. There are 75 questions in each test. Make sure you have not missed a page.

6. Start at question 1 and work your way to question 75.

7. If you are unable to complete a question leave it and go to the next one. Do not think about the question you have just left as this wastes time.

8. You may do rough work on the test pages.

9. Each test should take approximately 40 minutes.

10. When you have finished each test mark it with an adult who may be able to explain any questions that you do not understand.

Preparation for 11+ and 12+ tests
Non Verbal Reasoning Book 2
Multiple Choice   ISBN 1-873385-31-7

Test 06

ISBN 1-873385-31-7

Pupils Name

Test Date

1
- A ☐
- B ☐
- C ☐
- D ☐
- E ☐

2
- A ☐
- B ☐
- C ☐
- D ☐
- E ☐

3
- A ☐
- B ☐
- C ☐
- D ☐
- E ☐

4
- A ☐
- B ☐
- C ☐
- D ☐
- E ☐

5
- A ☐
- B ☐
- C ☐
- D ☐
- E ☐

6
- A ☐
- B ☐
- C ☐
- D ☐
- E ☐

Example
- 10 ■
- 12 ☐
- 8 ☐
- 15 ☐
- 6 ☐

7
- 28 ☐
- 32 ☐
- 14 ☐
- 19 ☐
- 36 ☐

8
- 2 ☐
- 60 ☐
- 65 ☐
- 12 ☐
- 19 ☐

9
- 19 ☐
- 10 ☐
- 12 ☐
- 25 ☐
- 21 ☐

10
- 45 ☐
- 36 ☐
- 42 ☐
- 49 ☐
- 32 ☐

11
- 52 ☐
- 49 ☐
- 54 ☐
- 47 ☐
- 43 ☐

12
- 8 ☐
- 10 ☐
- 12 ☐
- 9 ☐
- 7 ☐

Example
- A ☐
- B ■
- C ☐
- D ☐

13
- A ☐
- B ☐
- C ☐
- D ☐

14
- A ☐
- B ☐
- C ☐
- D ☐

15
- A ☐
- B ☐
- C ☐
- D ☐

16
- A ☐
- B ☐
- C ☐
- D ☐

17
- A ☐
- B ☐
- C ☐
- D ☐

18
- A ☐
- B ☐
- C ☐
- D ☐

19
- 48 ☐
- 50 ☐
- 52 ☐
- 49 ☐
- 47 ☐

20
- 900 ☐
- 890 ☐
- 970 ☐
- 1000 ☐
- 1200 ☐

21
- 7.2 ☐
- 7.4 ☐
- 7.6 ☐
- 8.0 ☐
- 8.2 ☐

22
- 64 ☐
- 66 ☐
- 69 ☐
- 65 ☐
- 63 ☐

23
- 202.5 ☐
- 203 ☐
- 202 ☐
- 201.5 ☐
- 201 ☐

24
- 46 ☐
- 49 ☐
- 47 ☐
- 50 ☐
- 52 ☐

Example
- A ☐
- B ☐
- C ☐
- D ■

25
- A ☐
- B ☐
- C ☐
- D ☐

26
- A ☐
- B ☐
- C ☐
- D ☐

27
- A ☐
- B ☐
- C ☐
- D ☐

28
- A ☐
- B ☐
- C ☐
- D ☐

29
- A ☐
- B ☐
- C ☐
- D ☐

30
- A ☐
- B ☐
- C ☐
- D ☐

31
- A ☐
- B ☐
- C ☐
- D ☐

32
- A ☐
- B ☐
- C ☐
- D ☐

33
- A ☐
- B ☐
- C ☐
- D ☐

34
- A ☐
- B ☐
- C ☐
- D ☐

35
- A ☐
- B ☐
- C ☐
- D ☐

36
- 45 ☐
- 30 ☐
- 46 ☐
- 44 ☐
- 42 ☐

37
- 40 ☐
- 39 ☐
- 41 ☐
- 42 ☐
- 44 ☐

38
- 29 ☐
- 30 ☐
- 32 ☐
- 28 ☐
- 31 ☐

Please mark boxes with a single line ▬ Do not mark outside the boxes

Example
- A ☐
- B ☐
- C ☐
- D ☐
- E ▬

39
- A ☐
- B ☐
- C ☐
- D ☐
- E ☐

40
- A ☐
- B ☐
- C ☐
- D ☐
- E ☐

41
- A ☐
- B ☐
- C ☐
- D ☐
- E ☐

42
- A ☐
- B ☐
- C ☐
- D ☐
- E ☐

43
- A ☐
- B ☐
- C ☐
- D ☐
- E ☐

44
- A ☐
- B ☐
- C ☐
- D ☐
- E ☐

45
- A ☐
- B ☐
- C ☐
- D ☐
- E ☐

46
- A ☐
- B ☐
- C ☐
- D ☐
- E ☐

47
- A ☐
- B ☐
- C ☐
- D ☐
- E ☐

48
- A ☐
- B ☐
- C ☐
- D ☐
- E ☐

49
- 1275 ☐
- 1325 ☐
- 1400 ☐
- 1220 ☐

50
- 7.5 ☐
- -7.5 ☐
- 6.0 ☐
- -5.5 ☐

51
- 12 ☐
- 13 ☐
- 11 ☐
- 17 ☐

52
- 0.75 ☐
- 1.75 ☐
- 2.25 ☐
- 1.40 ☐

53
- 2.25 ☐
- 1.15 ☐
- 3.50 ☐
- 1.10 ☐

54
- 0.10 ☐
- 5.00 ☐
- 0.75 ☐
- 2.25 ☐

55
- 5 ☐
- 6 ☐
- 8 ☐
- 14 ☐

56
- 2.25 ☐
- -0.25 ☐
- -1.40 ☐
- -6.30 ☐

57
- $1/3$ ☐
- $4/8$ ☐
- $2/3$ ☐
- $5/6$ ☐

58
- $3/7$ ☐
- $4/8$ ☐
- $6/9$ ☐
- $2/5$ ☐

59
- $1/2$ ☐
- $1/7$ ☐
- $6/7$ ☐
- $5/8$ ☐

60
- $1/3$ ☐
- $3/4$ ☐
- $2/3$ ☐
- $1/6$ ☐

61
- $1/3$ ☐
- $5/6$ ☐
- $1/2$ ☐
- $1/4$ ☐

62
- $3/4$ ☐
- $1/4$ ☐
- $5/6$ ☐
- $1/8$ ☐

63
- 12 ☐
- 10 ☐
- 8 ☐
- 9 ☐

64
- 0 ☐
- 2 ☐
- 1 ☐
- 3 ☐

65
- 2 ☐
- 4 ☐
- 5 ☐
- 3 ☐

66
- 5 ☐
- 4 ☐
- 6 ☐
- 7 ☐

67
- 1 ☐
- 4 ☐
- 3 ☐
- 5 ☐

68
- 0 ☐
- 5 ☐
- 3 ☐
- 4 ☐

69
- 5 ☐
- 6 ☐
- 4 ☐
- 3 ☐

70
- 4 ☐
- 7 ☐
- 5 ☐
- 3 ☐

71
- 0 ☐
- 1 ☐
- 3 ☐
- 4 ☐

72
- 1 ☐
- 3 ☐
- 4 ☐
- 2 ☐

73
- 4 ☐
- 5 ☐
- 7 ☐
- 6 ☐

74
- 3 ☐
- 1 ☐
- 4 ☐
- 6 ☐

75
- 2 ☐
- 1 ☐
- 0 ☐
- 3 ☐

TEST 06

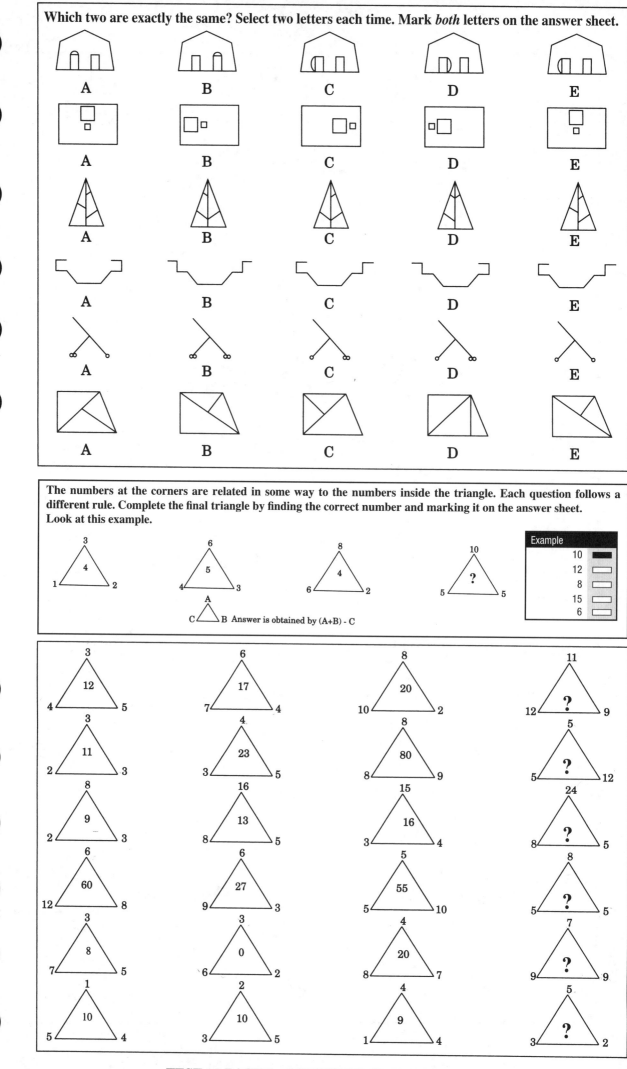

TEST 06 PAGE 1 – MULTIPLE CHOICE

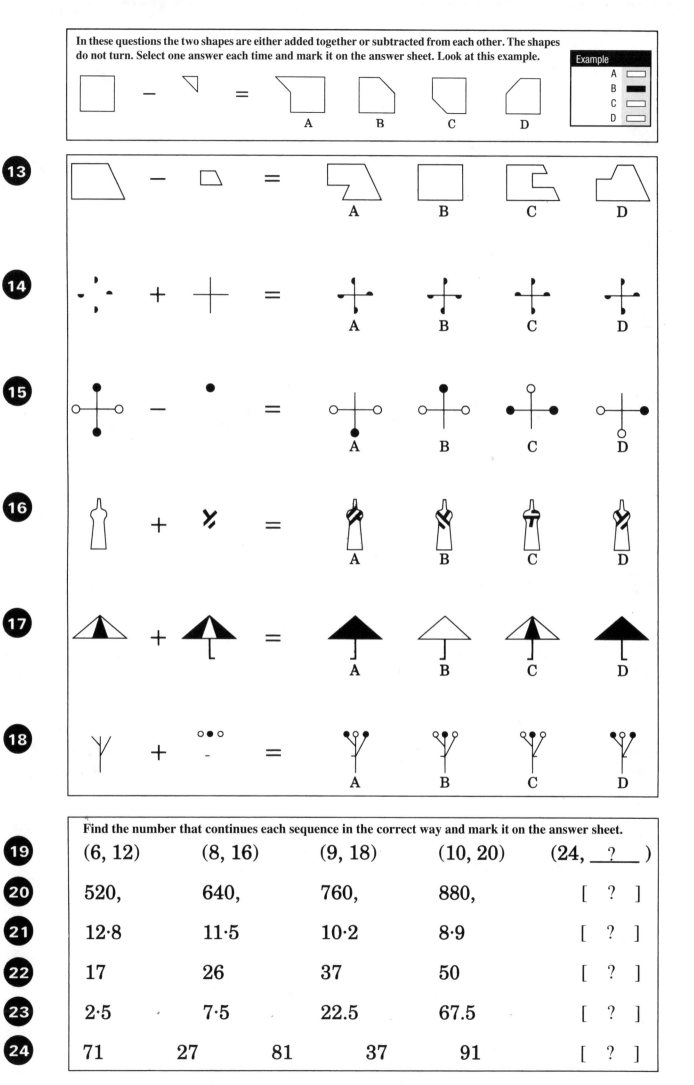

In these questions the two shapes are either added together or subtracted from each other. The shapes do not turn. Select one answer each time and mark it on the answer sheet. Look at this example.

Example

13

14

15

16

17

18

Find the number that continues each sequence in the correct way and mark it on the answer sheet.

19	(6, 12)	(8, 16)	(9, 18)	(10, 20)	(24, __?__)
20	520,	640,	760,	880,	[?]
21	12·8	11·5	10·2	8·9	[?]
22	17	26	37	50	[?]
23	2·5	7·5	22.5	67.5	[?]
24	71	27	81	37	91	[?]

TEST 06 PAGE 2 – MULTIPLE CHOICE

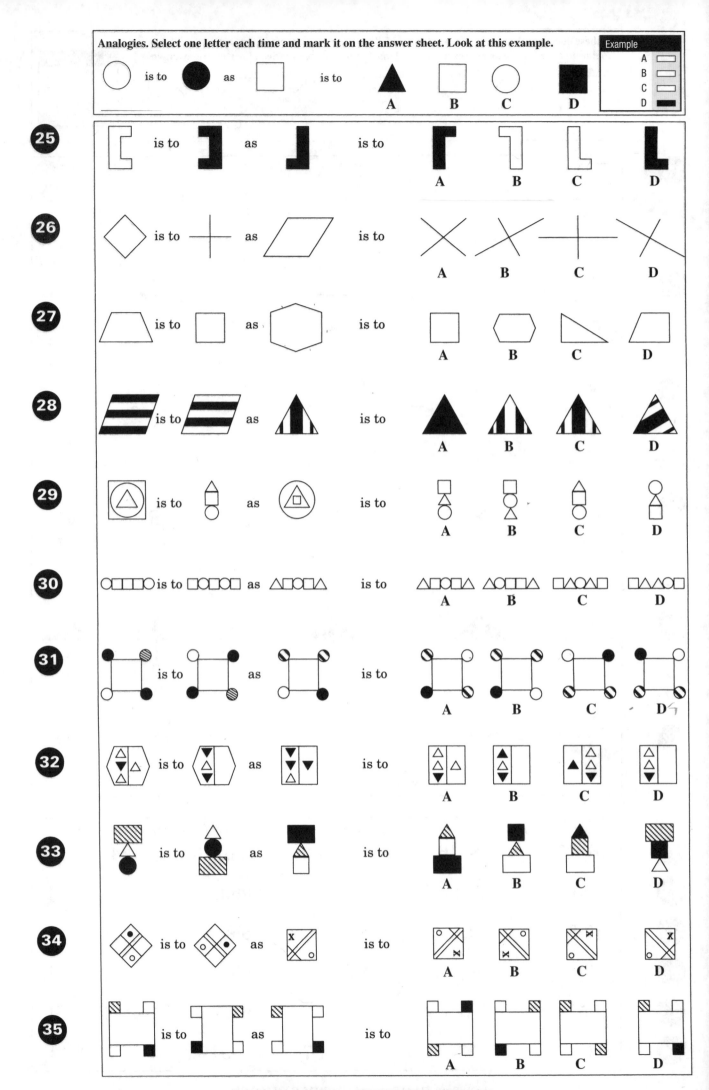

The numbers in the right hand column are connected to those in the left hand column. Each question follows a different rule. Select the correct answer to complete the brackets and mark it on the answer sheet.

36

6 ——→ 18

8 ——→ 24

10 ——→ 30

15 ——→ (_?_)

37

26 ——→ 13

34 ——→ 17

56 ——→ 28

82 ——→ (_?_)

38

4 ——→ 1

36 ——→ 9

44 ——→ 11

120 ——→ (_?_)

Which shape is the same but facing the opposite direction? Select one letter each time and mark it on the answer sheet. Look at this example.

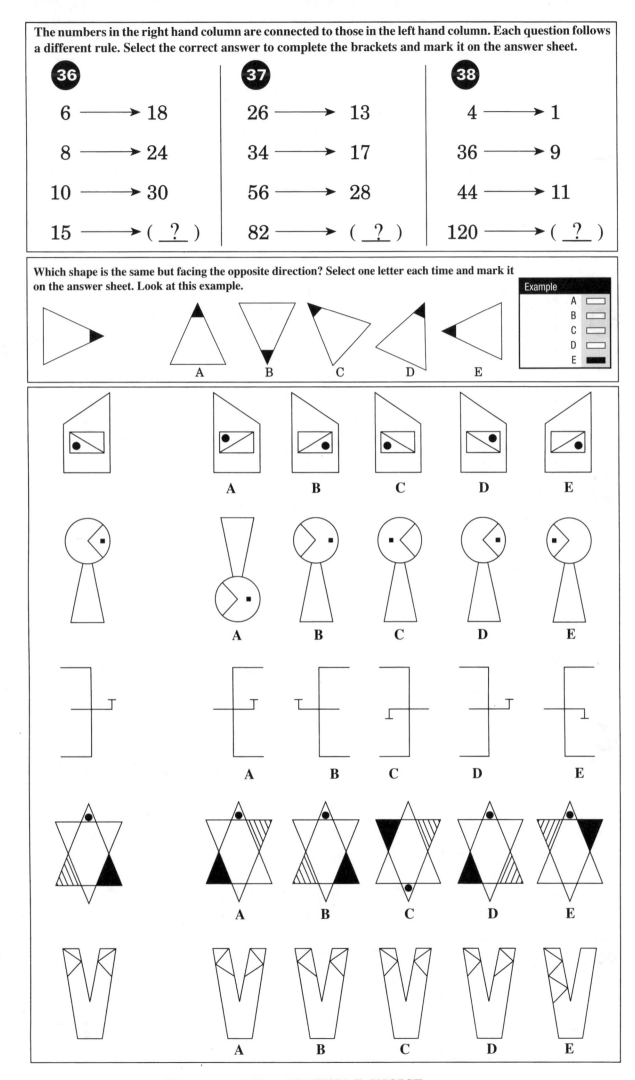

39

A B C D E

40

A B C D E

41

A B C D E

42

A B C D E

43

A B C D E

TEST 06 PAGE 4 – MULTIPLE CHOICE

Looking from point 'X' what will you see? Select one letter each time and mark it on the answer sheet.

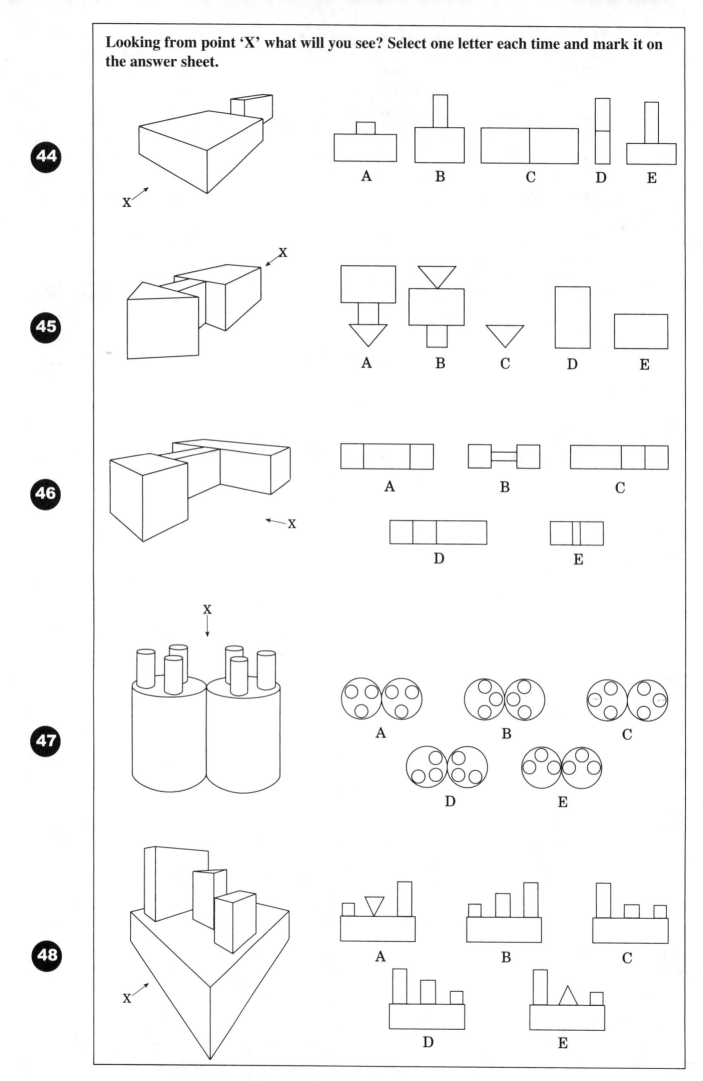

What number is the arrow pointing to? Select one answer from the box on the right and mark it on the answer sheet.

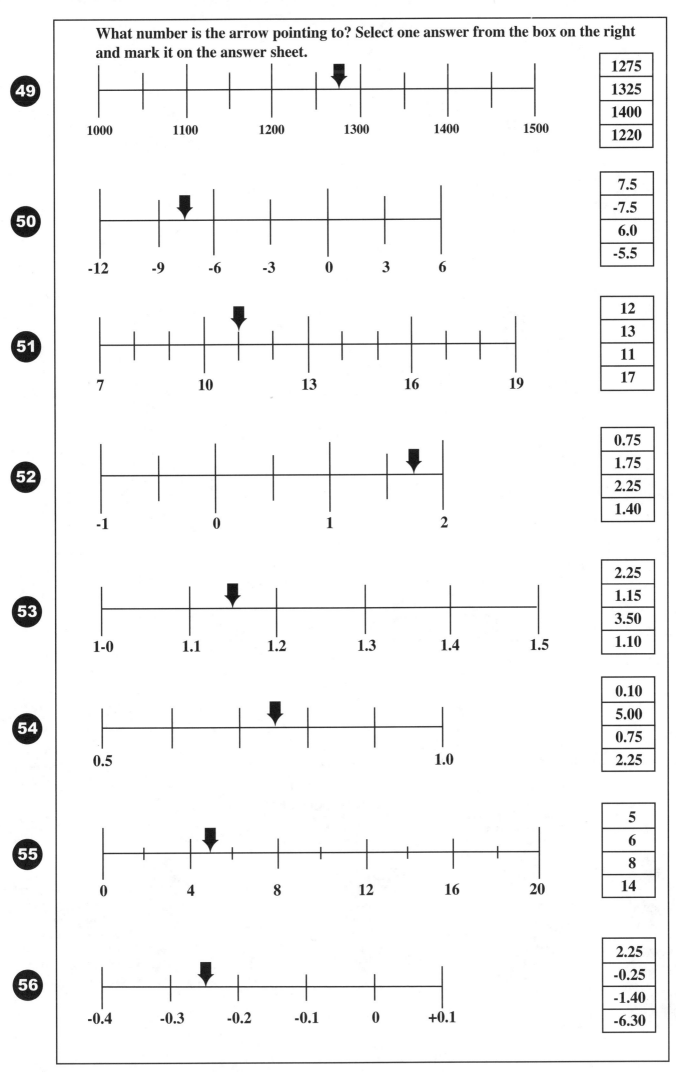

49

1275
1325
1400
1220

50

7.5
-7.5
6.0
-5.5

51

12
13
11
17

52

0.75
1.75
2.25
1.40

53

2.25
1.15
3.50
1.10

54

0.10
5.00
0.75
2.25

55

5
6
8
14

56

2.25
-0.25
-1.40
-6.30

What fraction is shaded each time? Select one answer and mark it on the answer sheet.

 57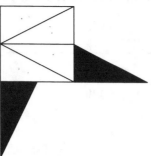

$$\frac{1}{3} \quad \frac{4}{8} \quad \frac{2}{3} \quad \frac{5}{6}$$

58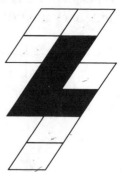

$$\frac{3}{7} \quad \frac{4}{8} \quad \frac{6}{9} \quad \frac{2}{5}$$

59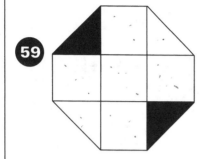

$$\frac{1}{2} \quad \frac{1}{7} \quad \frac{6}{7} \quad \frac{5}{8}$$

60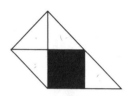

$$\frac{1}{3} \quad \frac{3}{4} \quad \frac{2}{3} \quad \frac{1}{6}$$

61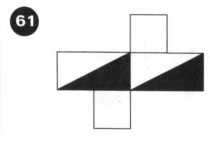

$$\frac{1}{3} \quad \frac{5}{6} \quad \frac{1}{2} \quad \frac{1}{4}$$

62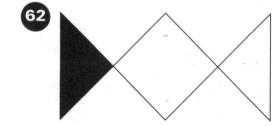

$$\frac{3}{4} \quad \frac{1}{4} \quad \frac{5}{6} \quad \frac{1}{8}$$

Complete this mathematical table by dividing the left hand column into the top row. Mark your answers on the answer sheet.

63

64

65 66

67 68

÷	6	
6		2
	3	
	2	

Supply the missing numbers in these sums. Mark your answer on the answer sheet.

69 70

71

72

```
        2  7  8
        □  □  4
     +  3  1  □
     _____
   □  2  4  3
```

73   2 ⟌ □ 4 9

74   3 7 □

75   Rem □

Preparation for 11+ and 12+ tests
Non Verbal Reasoning Book 2
Multiple Choice   ISBN 1-873385-31-7

Test 07

Pupils Name

Test Date

1
A
B
C
D
E

2
A
B
C
D
E

3
A
B
C
D
E

4
A
B
C
D
E

5
A
B
C
D
E

6
A
B
C
D
E

7
A
B
C
D
E

8
A
B
C
D
E

Example
A
B
C
D ▬

9
A
B
C
D

10
A
B
C
D

11
A
B
C
D

12
A
B
C
D

13
A
B
C
D

14
A
B
C
D

15
A
B
C
D

16
A
B
C
D

17
A
B
C
D

18
A
B
C
D

19
A
B
C
D
E

20
A
B
C
D
E

21
A
B
C
D
E

22
A
B
C
D
E

23
A
B
C
D
E

24
A
B
C
D
E

25
A
B
C
D
E

26
A
B
C
D
E

27
A
B
C
D
E

28
A
B
C
D
E

Example
A
B
C
D ▬
E
F

29
A
B
C
D
E
F

30
A
B
C
D
E
F

31
A
B
C
D
E
F

32
A
B
C
D
E
F

33
A
B
C
D
E
F

34
A
B
C
D
E
F

35
A
B
C
D
E
F

36
A
B
C
D
E
F

37
A
B
C
D
E
F

38
A
B
C
D
E
F

Please Turn Over

Please mark boxes with a single line ▬ Do not mark outside the boxes

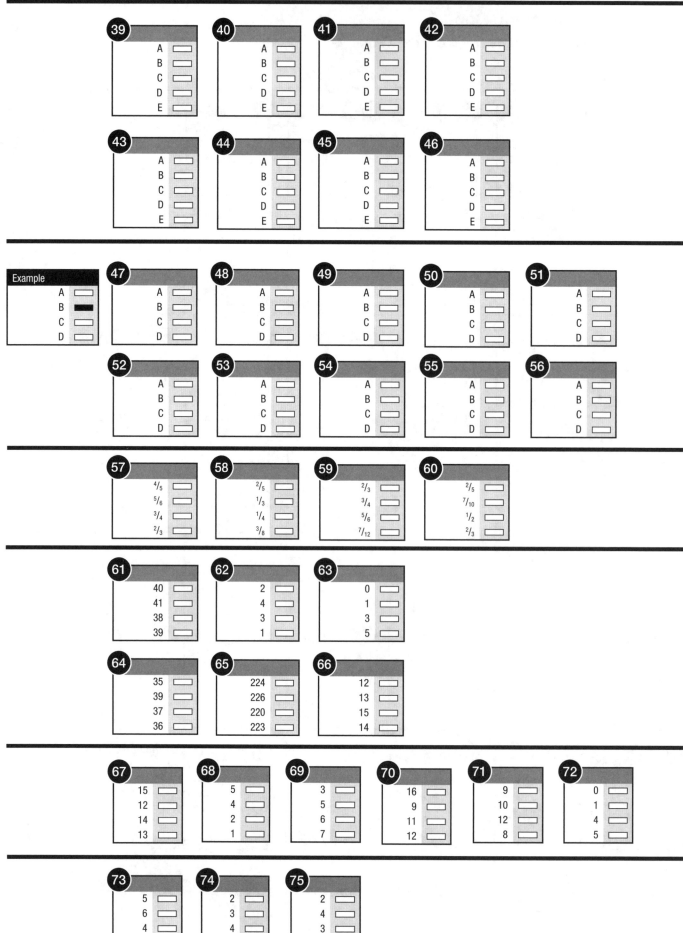

TEST 07

SCORE _____

Which two are exactly the same? Select two letters each time and mark *both* letters on the answer sheet.

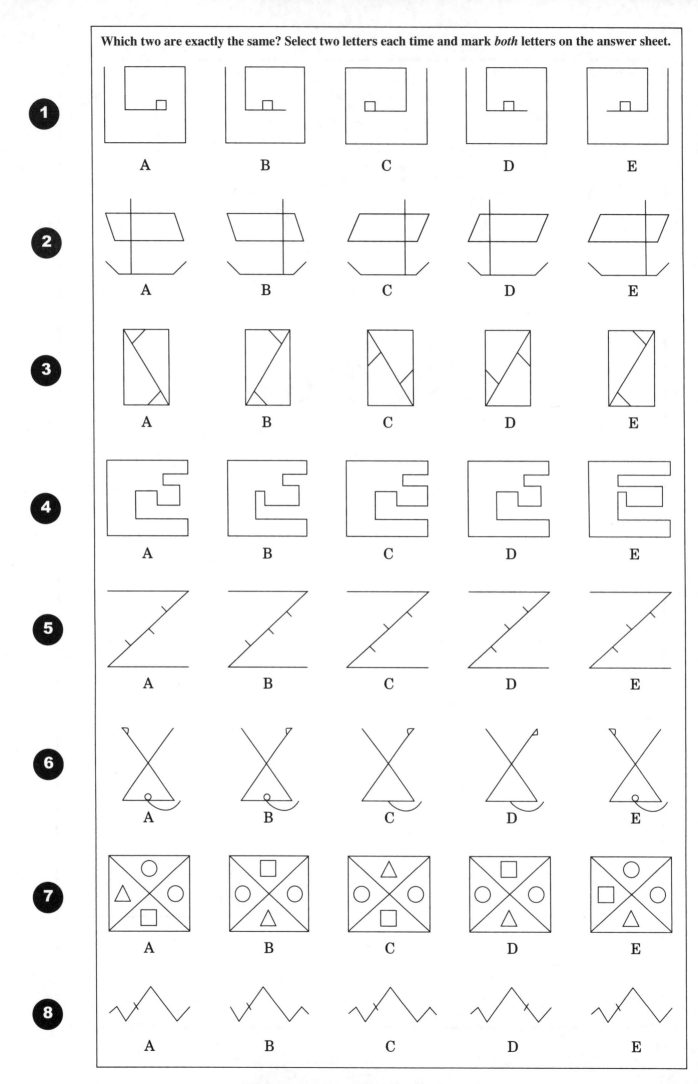

Which shape is the same but facing the opposite direction. Select one letter
each time and mark it on the answer sheet. Look at this example.

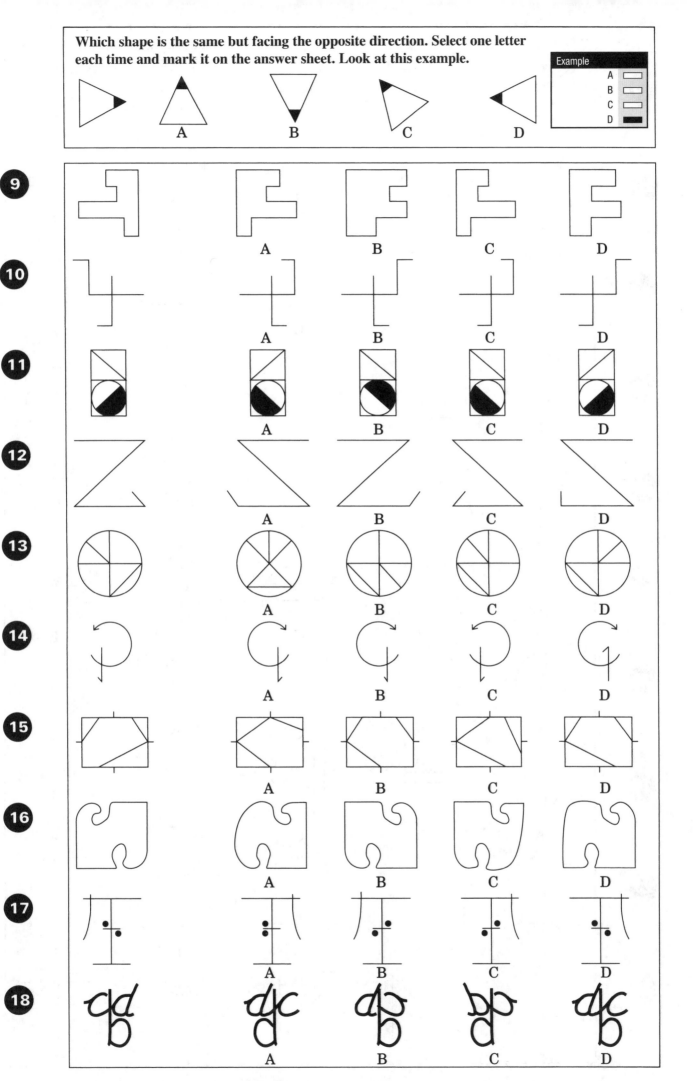

Which shape is different from the other four? Select one letter each time and mark it on the answer sheet.

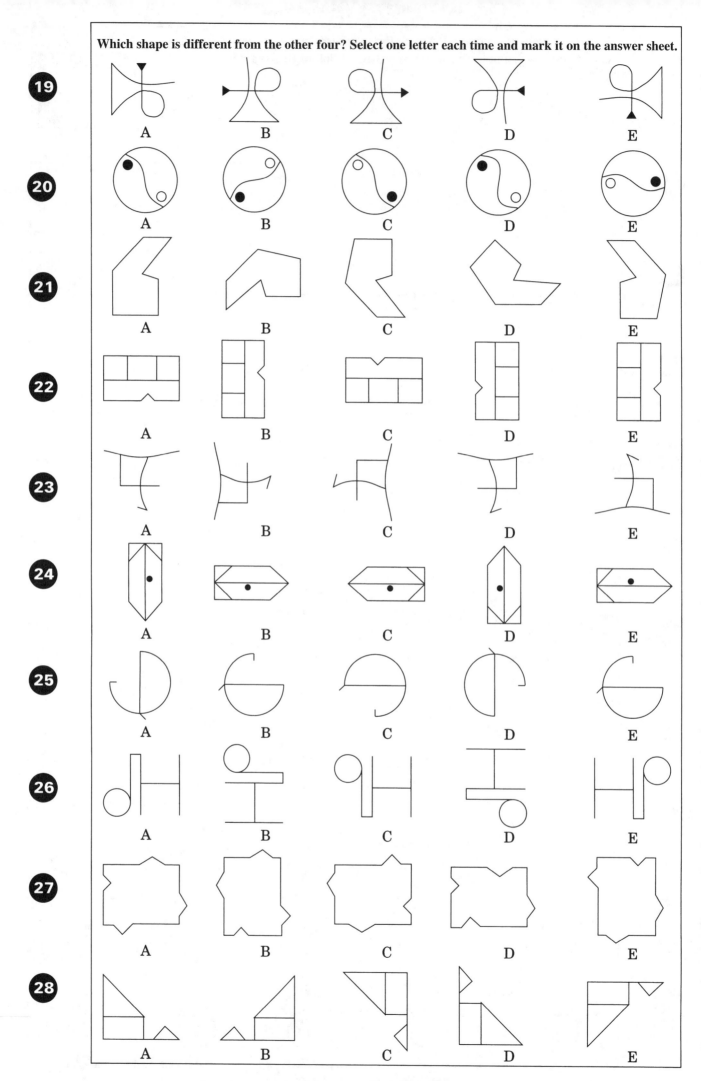

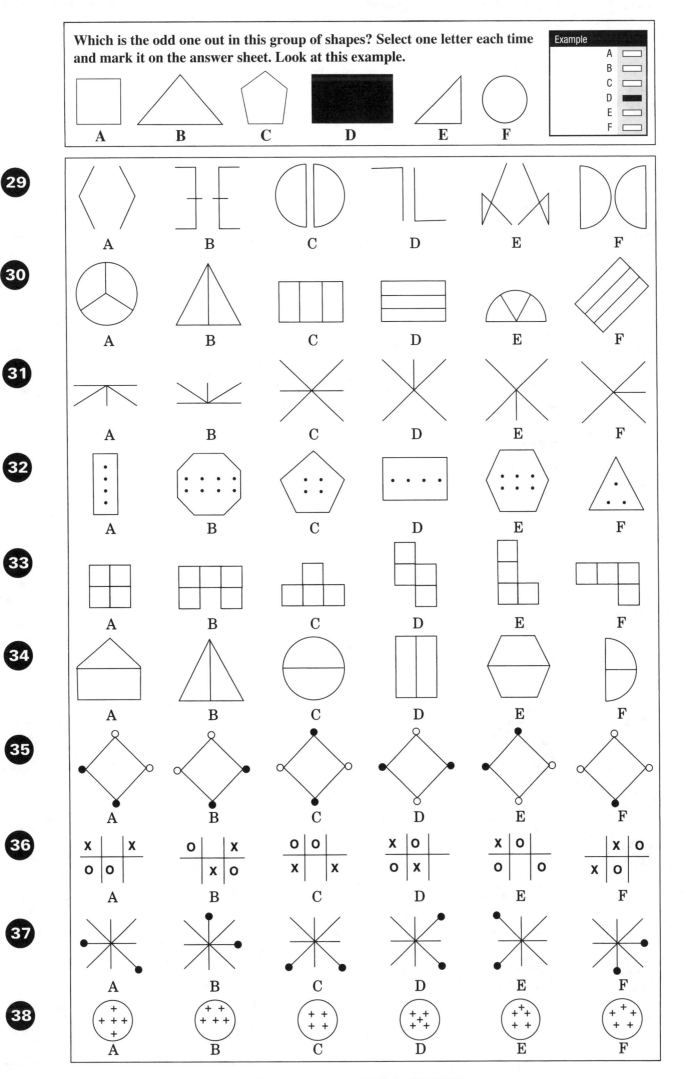

Without turning the pieces over choose which piece completes the white jig-saw.
Select one letter each time and mark it on the answer sheet.

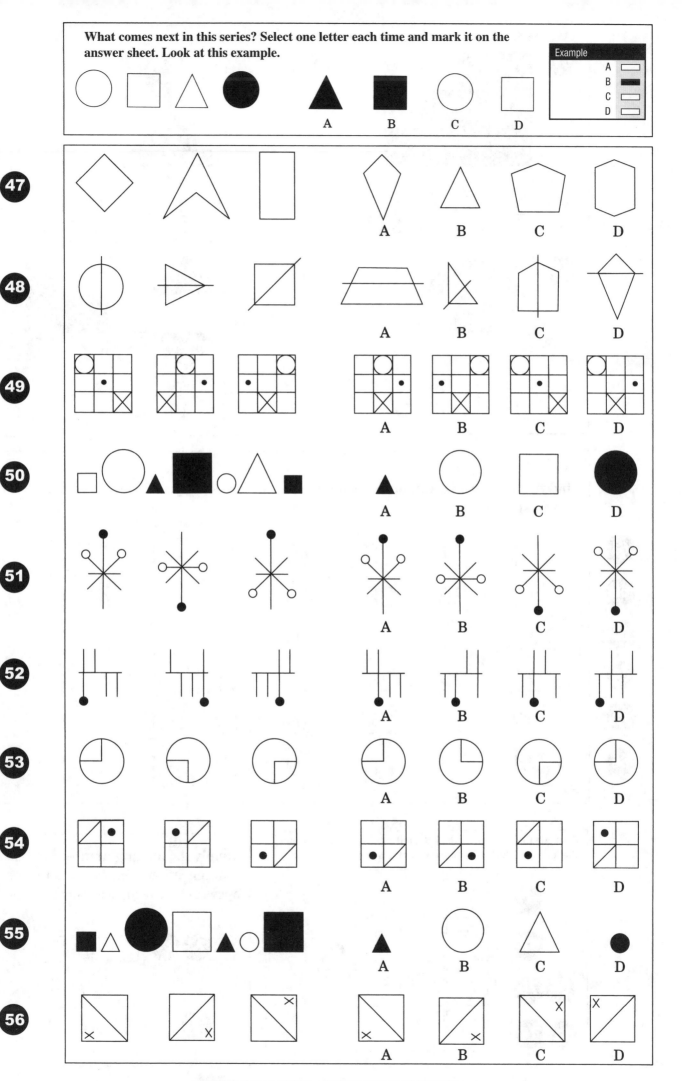

What fraction is shaded each time? Select one answer and mark it on your answer sheet.

57

$\frac{4}{5}$ $\frac{5}{6}$ $\frac{3}{4}$ $\frac{2}{3}$

58

$\frac{2}{5}$ $\frac{1}{3}$ $\frac{1}{4}$ $\frac{3}{8}$

59

$\frac{2}{3}$ $\frac{3}{4}$ $\frac{5}{6}$ $\frac{7}{12}$

60

$\frac{2}{5}$ $\frac{7}{10}$ $\frac{1}{2}$ $\frac{2}{3}$

Find the number that continues each series in the correct way and mark it on the answer sheet.

61   4   11   18   25   32   [?]

62   44   36   28   20   12   [?]

63   243   81   27   9   3   [?]

64   21   22   24   27   31   [?]

65   7   14   28   56   112   [?]

66   4   5   8   9   12   [?]

Subtract the numbers in the left hand column from those in the top row. Mark your answers on the answer sheet.

−	11	
7		7
	8	
		4

67 **68** **69** **70** **71** **72**

Supply the missing numbers in this multiplication sum. Mark your answers on the answer sheet.

73 **74**

$$\begin{array}{r} \square\,4\,\square \\ \times\ 7 \\ \hline \square\,8\,0\,1 \end{array}$$

75

TEST 07 PAGE 7 – MULTIPLE CHOICE

Pupils Name

Test Date

Example
A
B
C ■
D
E
F

1
A
B
C
D
E
F

2
A
B
C
D
E
F

3
A
B
C
D
E
F

4
A
B
C
D
E
F

5
A
B
C
D
E
F

6
A
B
C
D
E
F

7
A
B
C
D
E
F

8
A
B
C
D
E
F

9
12
10
9
11

10
60
62
64
66

11
20
24
21
22

Example
A
B ■
C
D

12
A
B
C
D

13
A
B
C
D

14
A
B
C
D

15
A
B
C
D

16
A
B
C
D

17
A
B
C
D

18
A
B
C
D

19
A
B
C
D

Example
A
B ■
C
D

20
A
B
C
D

21
A
B
C
D

22
A
B
C
D

23
A
B
C
D

24
A
B
C
D

25
A
B
C
D

26
A
B
C
D

27
A
B
C
D

28
A
B
C
D
E
F

29
A
B
C
D
E
F

30
A
B
C
D
E
F

31
A
B
C
D
E
F

32
A
B
C
D
E
F

33
A
B
C
D
E
F

Please Turn Over

Please mark boxes with a single line ▬ Do not mark outside the boxes

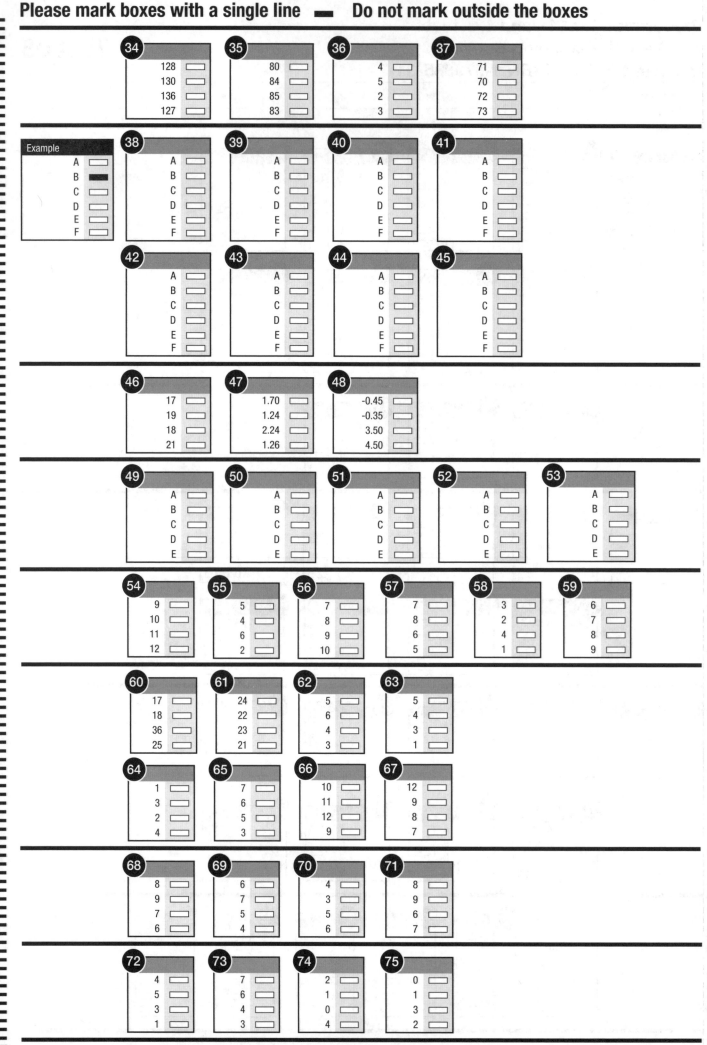

34
128 ▭
130 ▭
136 ▭
127 ▭

35
80 ▭
84 ▭
85 ▭
83 ▭

36
4 ▭
5 ▭
2 ▭
3 ▭

37
71 ▭
70 ▭
72 ▭
73 ▭

Example
A ▭
B ▬▬
C ▭
D ▭
E ▭
F ▭

38
A ▭
B ▭
C ▭
D ▭
E ▭
F ▭

39
A ▭
B ▭
C ▭
D ▭
E ▭
F ▭

40
A ▭
B ▭
C ▭
D ▭
E ▭
F ▭

41
A ▭
B ▭
C ▭
D ▭
E ▭
F ▭

42
A ▭
B ▭
C ▭
D ▭
E ▭
F ▭

43
A ▭
B ▭
C ▭
D ▭
E ▭
F ▭

44
A ▭
B ▭
C ▭
D ▭
E ▭
F ▭

45
A ▭
B ▭
C ▭
D ▭
E ▭
F ▭

46
17 ▭
19 ▭
18 ▭
21 ▭

47
1.70 ▭
1.24 ▭
2.24 ▭
1.26 ▭

48
-0.45 ▭
-0.35 ▭
3.50 ▭
4.50 ▭

49
A ▭
B ▭
C ▭
D ▭
E ▭

50
A ▭
B ▭
C ▭
D ▭
E ▭

51
A ▭
B ▭
C ▭
D ▭
E ▭

52
A ▭
B ▭
C ▭
D ▭
E ▭

53
A ▭
B ▭
C ▭
D ▭
E ▭

54
9 ▭
10 ▭
11 ▭
12 ▭

55
5 ▭
4 ▭
6 ▭
2 ▭

56
7 ▭
8 ▭
9 ▭
10 ▭

57
7 ▭
8 ▭
6 ▭
5 ▭

58
3 ▭
2 ▭
4 ▭
1 ▭

59
6 ▭
7 ▭
8 ▭
9 ▭

60
17 ▭
18 ▭
36 ▭
25 ▭

61
24 ▭
22 ▭
23 ▭
21 ▭

62
5 ▭
6 ▭
4 ▭
3 ▭

63
5 ▭
4 ▭
3 ▭
1 ▭

64
1 ▭
3 ▭
2 ▭
4 ▭

65
7 ▭
6 ▭
5 ▭
3 ▭

66
10 ▭
11 ▭
12 ▭
9 ▭

67
12 ▭
9 ▭
8 ▭
7 ▭

68
8 ▭
9 ▭
7 ▭
6 ▭

69
6 ▭
7 ▭
5 ▭
4 ▭

70
4 ▭
3 ▭
5 ▭
6 ▭

71
8 ▭
9 ▭
6 ▭
7 ▭

72
4 ▭
5 ▭
3 ▭
1 ▭

73
7 ▭
6 ▭
4 ▭
3 ▭

74
2 ▭
1 ▭
0 ▭
4 ▭

75
0 ▭
1 ▭
3 ▭
2 ▭

TEST 08

SCORE _____

Which is the odd one out in this group of shapes? Select one letter each time and mark it on the answer sheet. Look at this example.

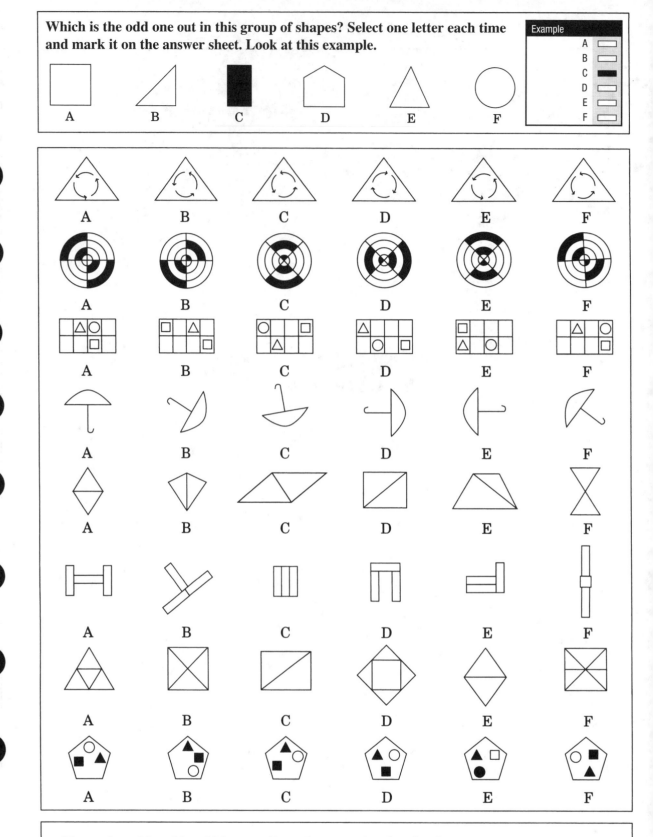

Given that 16 × 12 = 192, complete the equation by finding the missing number that goes in the bracket. Mark your answer on the answer sheet.

9   17 x 12 = 192 + (_?_)

10   16 x 8 + (_?_) = 192

11   192 - (_?_) = 12 x 14

Look at the shape on the left. Which shadow matches the shape on the left exactly?
Select one letter each time and mark it on the answer sheet.
Look at this example.

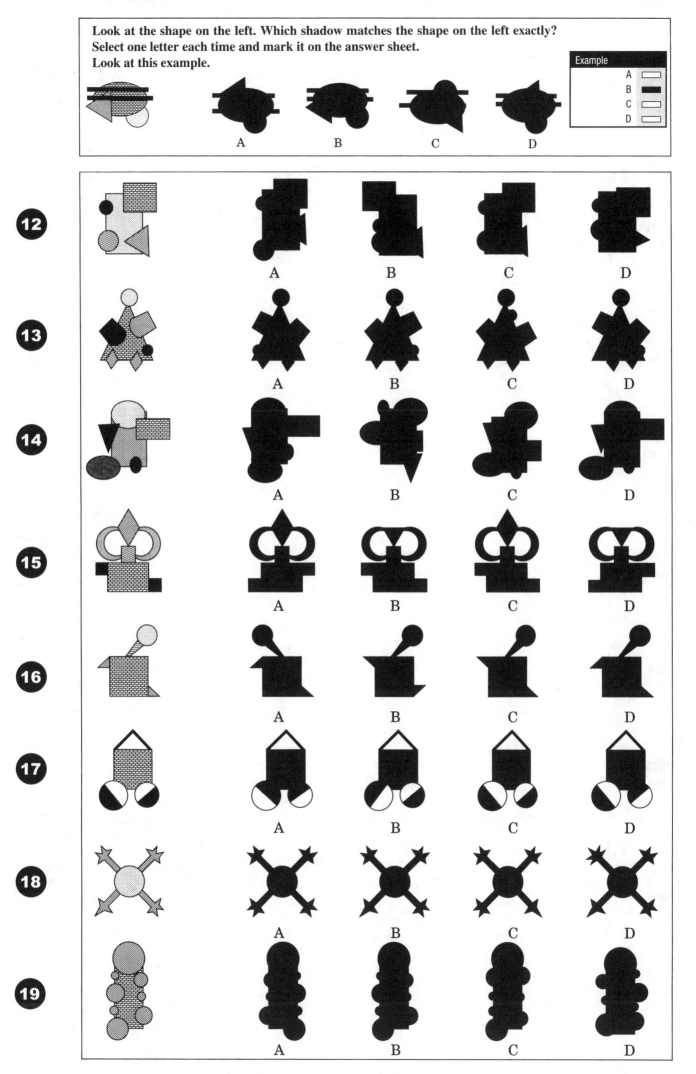

TEST 08 PAGE 2 – MULTIPLE CHOICE

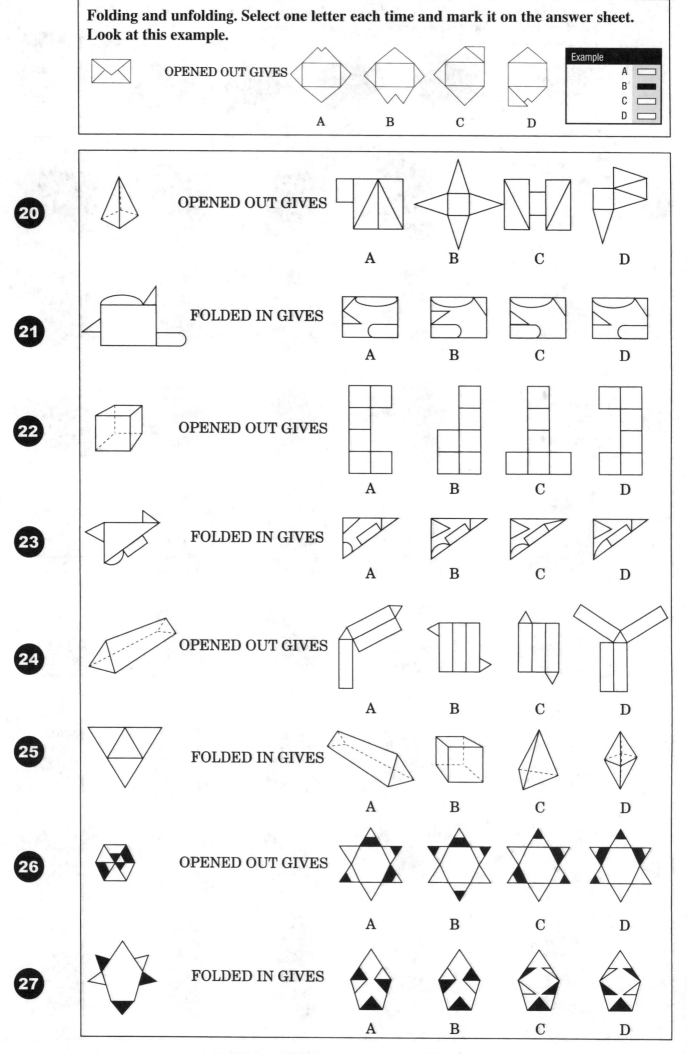

TEST 08 PAGE 3 – MULTIPLE CHOICE

Which two are exactly the same? Select two letters each time and mark *both* letters on the answer sheet.

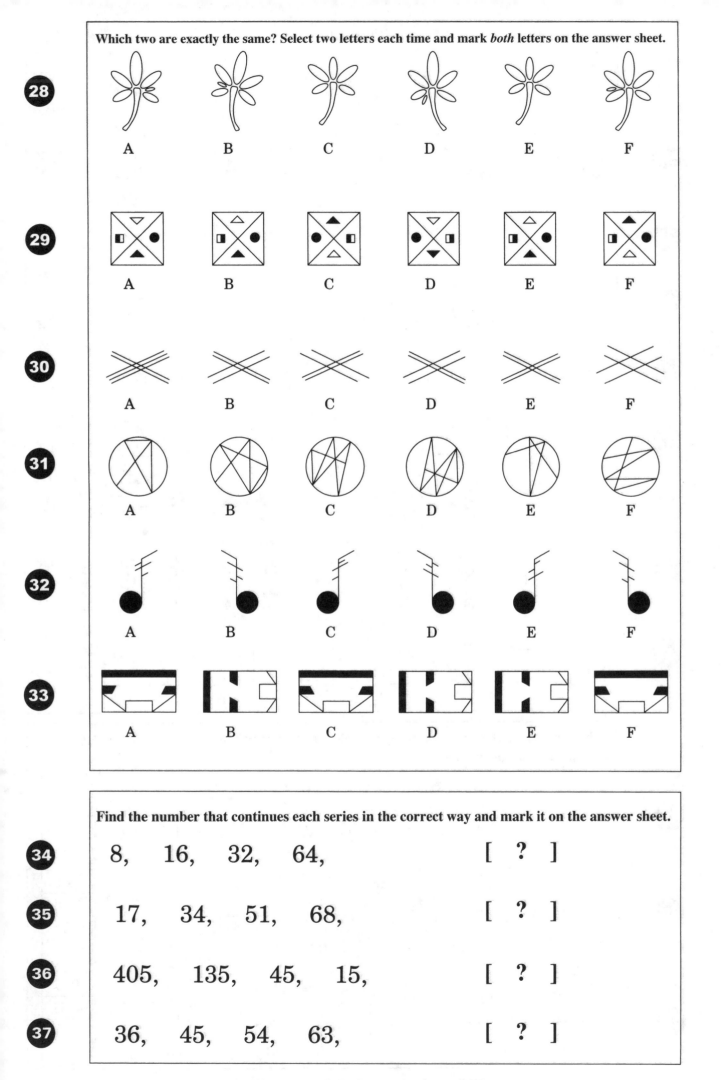

28
A B C D E F

29
A B C D E F

30
A B C D E F

31
A B C D E F

32
A B C D E F

33
A B C D E F

Find the number that continues each series in the correct way and mark it on the answer sheet.

34   8,   16,   32,   64,   [?]

35   17,   34,   51,   68,   [?]

36   405,   135,   45,   15,   [?]

37   36,   45,   54,   63,   [?]

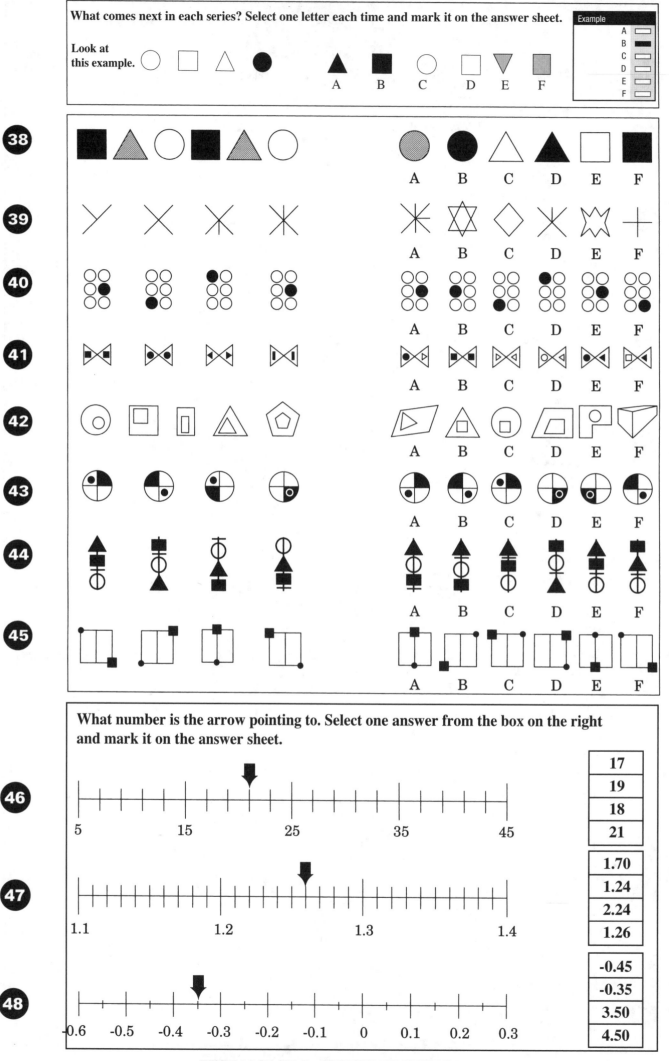

What comes next in each series? Select one letter each time and mark it on the answer sheet.

Look at this example.

38

39

40

41

42

43

44

45

What number is the arrow pointing to. Select one answer from the box on the right and mark it on the answer sheet.

46

5   15   25   35   45

| 17 |
| 19 |
| 18 |
| 21 |

47

1.1   1.2   1.3   1.4

| 1.70 |
| 1.24 |
| 2.24 |
| 1.26 |

48

-0.6 -0.5 -0.4 -0.3 -0.2 -0.1   0   0.1   0.2   0.3

| -0.45 |
| -0.35 |
| 3.50 |
| 4.50 |

Looking from point X what will you see? Select one letter each time and mark it on the answer sheet.

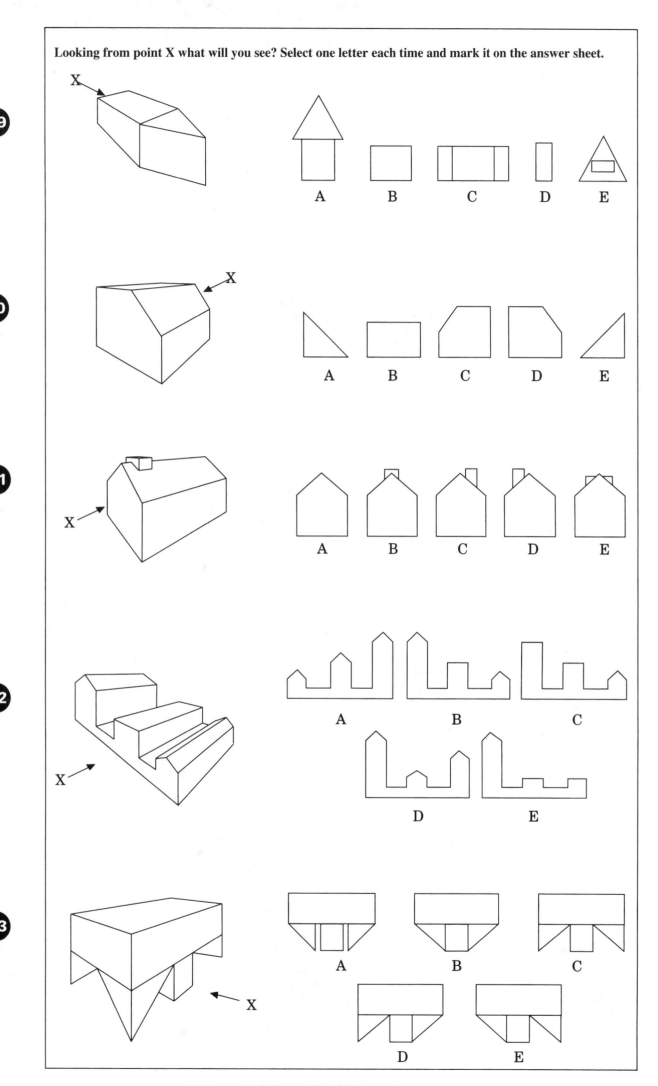

How many shapes like ▱ **are in the following shapes?**

Find the correct number and mark it on the answer sheet.

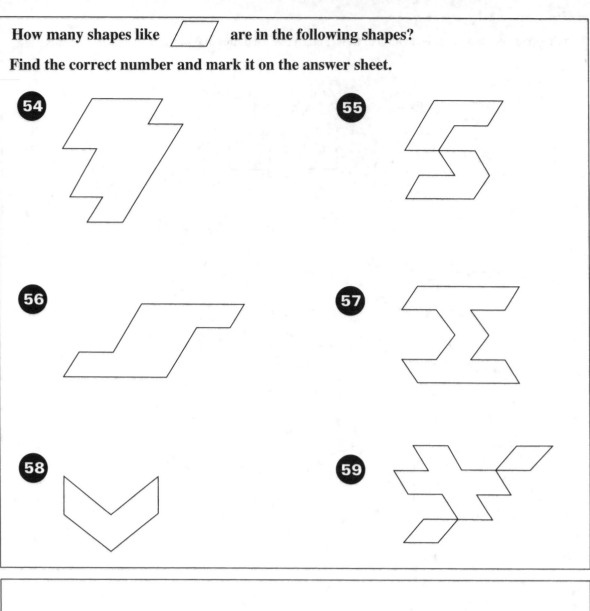

Complete this mathematical table
by dividing the left hand column
into the top row.
Mark your answers on the
answer sheet.

÷	12		
	2	6	
		18	
3	4		8

**Supply the missing numbers
in this subtraction sum.
Mark your answers on the answer sheet.**

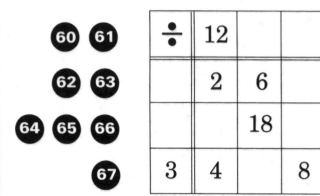

**Supply the missing numbers
in this addition sum.
Mark your answers on the answer sheet.**

(72)   7 ☐ 2
        4 1 8
(73) (74)   + ☐ 1 ☐
(75)   ☐ 8 8 0

Pupils Name

Test Date

Example
A
B
C
D ▬

1
A
B
C
D

2
A
B
C
D

3
A
B
C
D

4
A
B
C
D

5
A
B
C
D

6
A
B
C
D

7
A
B
C
D

8
A
B
C
D

Example
A
B
C ▬
D
E

9
A
B
C
D
E

10
A
B
C
D
E

11
A
B
C
D
E

12
A
B
C
D
E

13
A
B
C
D
E

14
A
B
C
D
E

15
A
B
C
D
E

16
A
B
C
D
E

17
A
B
C
D
E

18
A
B
C
D
E

19
8
9
10
11

20
10
12
11
9

21
11
10
8
9

22
8
9
11
12

23
11
12
14
15

24
10
11
12
13

25
45
47
48
49

26
20
21
23
24

27
28
29
26
27

28
6.3
6.4
6.2
6.1

29
21
23
25
26

30
7
8
9
10

Please Turn Over

Please mark boxes with a single line — Do not mark outside the boxes

Example
- A ☐
- B ▬
- C ☐
- D ☐

31
- A ☐
- B ☐
- C ☐
- D ☐
- E ☐

32
- A ☐
- B ☐
- C ☐
- D ☐
- E ☐

33
- A ☐
- B ☐
- C ☐
- D ☐

34
- A ☐
- B ☐
- C ☐
- D ☐

35
- A ☐
- B ☐
- C ☐
- D ☐

36
- A ☐
- B ☐
- C ☐
- D ☐

37
- A ☐
- B ☐
- C ☐
- D ☐

38
- A ☐
- B ☐
- C ☐
- D ☐

Example
- A ☐
- B ▬
- C ☐
- D ☐

39
- A ☐
- B ☐
- C ☐
- D ☐

40
- A ☐
- B ☐
- C ☐
- D ☐

41
- A ☐
- B ☐
- C ☐
- D ☐

42
- A ☐
- B ☐
- C ☐
- D ☐

43
- A ☐
- B ☐
- C ☐
- D ☐

44
- A ☐
- B ☐
- C ☐
- D ☐

45
- A ☐
- B ☐
- C ☐
- D ☐

46
- A ☐
- B ☐
- C ☐
- D ☐

47
- A ☐
- B ☐
- C ☐
- D ☐

48
- A ☐
- B ☐
- C ☐
- D ☐

Example
- A ☐
- B ☐
- C ☐
- D ▬
- E ☐

49
- A ☐
- B ☐
- C ☐
- D ☐
- E ☐

50
- A ☐
- B ☐
- C ☐
- D ☐
- E ☐

51
- A ☐
- B ☐
- C ☐
- D ☐
- E ☐

52
- A ☐
- B ☐
- C ☐
- D ☐
- E ☐

53
- A ☐
- B ☐
- C ☐
- D ☐
- E ☐

54
- A ☐
- B ☐
- C ☐
- D ☐
- E ☐

55
- A ☐
- B ☐
- C ☐
- D ☐
- E ☐

56
- A ☐
- B ☐
- C ☐
- D ☐
- E ☐

57
- A ☐
- B ☐
- C ☐
- D ☐
- E ☐

58
- A ☐
- B ☐
- C ☐
- D ☐
- E ☐

59
- $3/5$ ☐
- $2/3$ ☐
- $1/4$ ☐
- $5/9$ ☐

60
- $1/2$ ☐
- $1/3$ ☐
- $2/5$ ☐
- $1/4$ ☐

61
- $1/4$ ☐
- $1/3$ ☐
- $3/8$ ☐
- $2/5$ ☐

62
- $2/3$ ☐
- $3/4$ ☐
- $5/6$ ☐
- $4/5$ ☐

63
- $3/5$ ☐
- $2/3$ ☐
- $3/4$ ☐
- $7/10$ ☐

64
- $2/3$ ☐
- $1/3$ ☐
- $5/8$ ☐
- $2/5$ ☐

65
- 21 ☐
- 20 ☐
- 22 ☐
- 19 ☐

66
- 9 ☐
- 8 ☐
- 7 ☐
- 6 ☐

67
- 19 ☐
- 20 ☐
- 21 ☐
- 18 ☐

68
- 12 ☐
- 13 ☐
- 8 ☐
- 9 ☐

69
- 19 ☐
- 20 ☐
- 18 ☐
- 17 ☐

70
- 7 ☐
- 8 ☐
- 6 ☐
- 5 ☐

71
- 15 ☐
- 13 ☐
- 14 ☐
- 12 ☐

72
- 21 ☐
- 23 ☐
- 22 ☐
- 19 ☐

73
- 8 ☐
- 9 ☐
- 7 ☐
- 6 ☐

74
- 3 ☐
- 4 ☐
- 5 ☐
- 6 ☐

75
- 0 ☐
- 1 ☐
- 3 ☐
- 2 ☐

TEST 09

Which shape is the same but facing the opposite direction. Select one letter each time and mark it on the answer sheet. Look at this example.

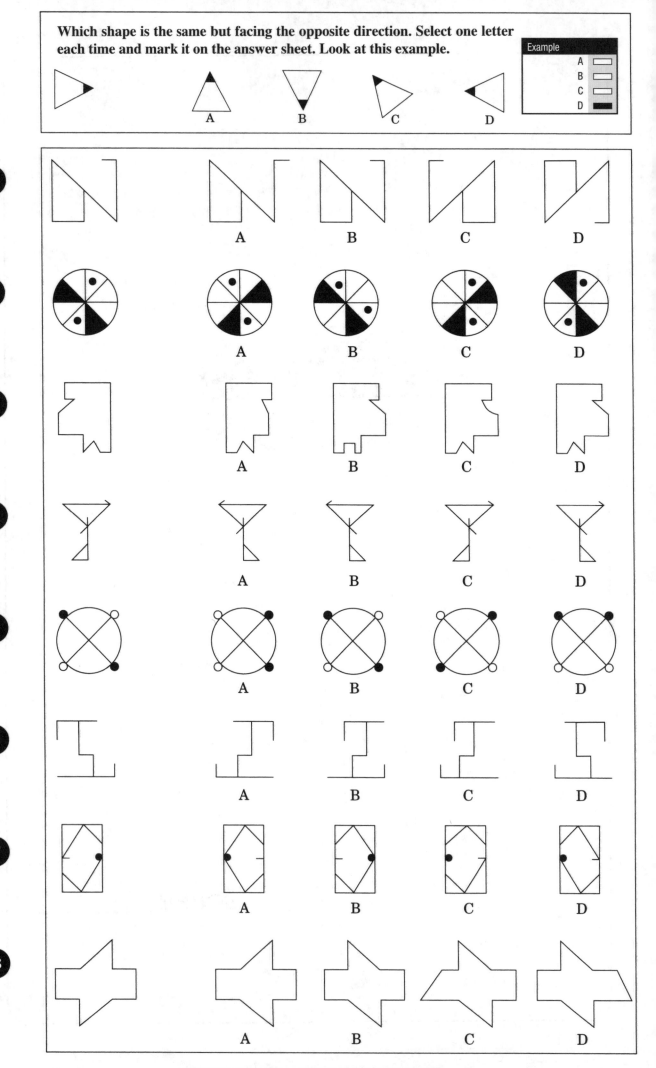

TEST 09 PAGE 1 – MULTIPLE CHOICE

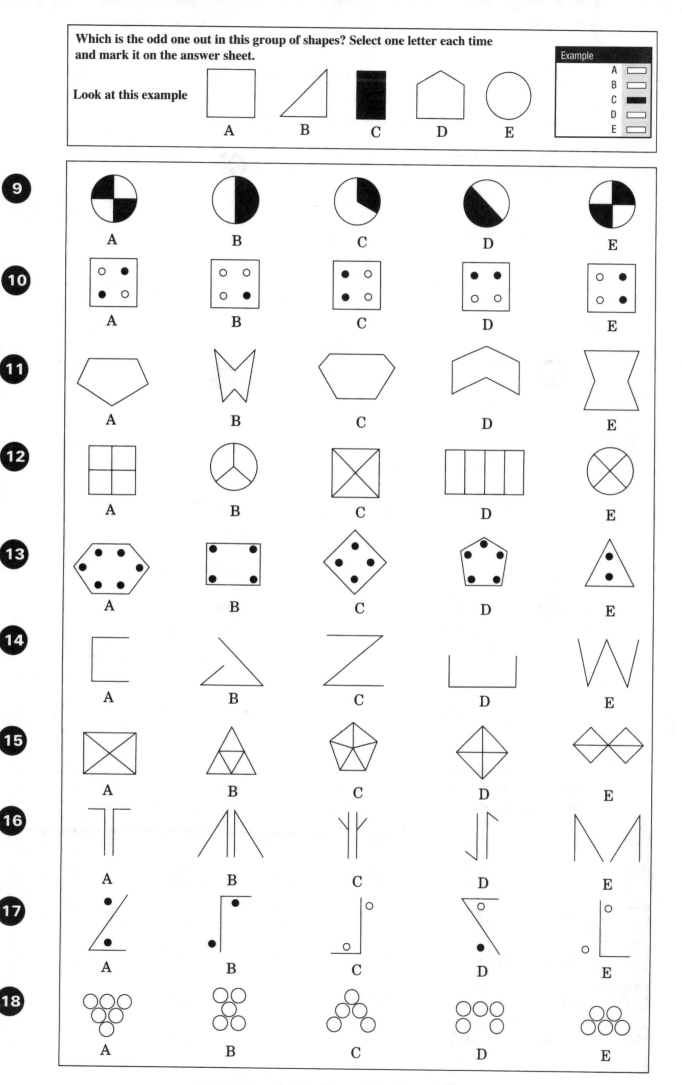

How many squares like 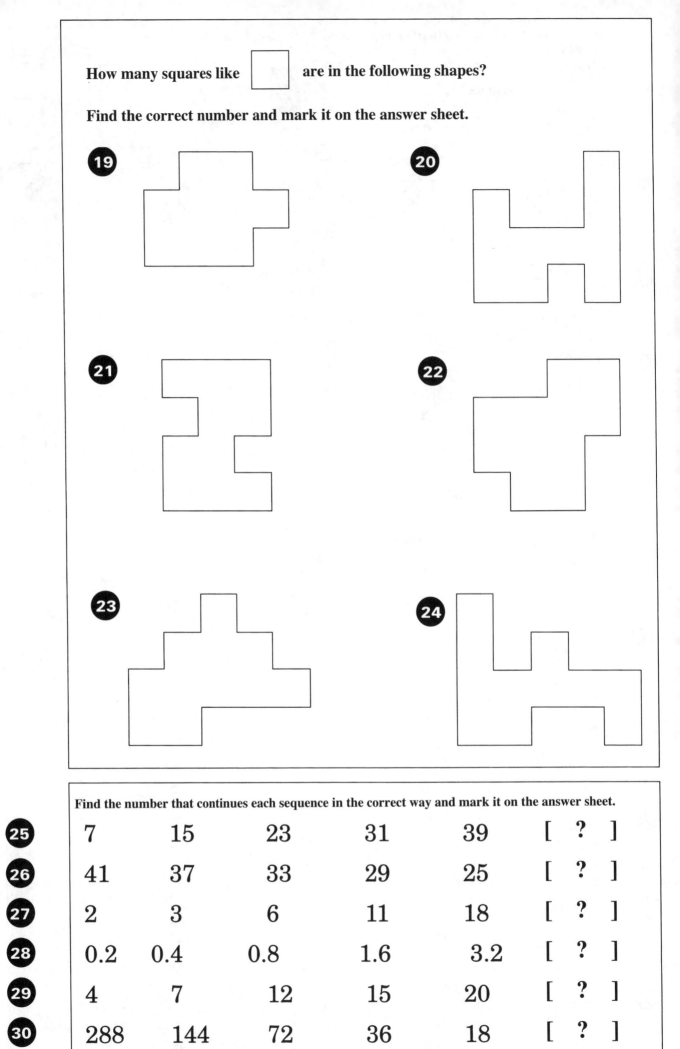 are in the following shapes?

Find the correct number and mark it on the answer sheet.

19

20

21

22

23

24

Find the number that continues each sequence in the correct way and mark it on the answer sheet.

25	7	15	23	31	39	[?]
26	41	37	33	29	25	[?]
27	2	3	6	11	18	[?]
28	0.2	0.4	0.8	1.6	3.2	[?]
29	4	7	12	15	20	[?]
30	288	144	72	36	18	[?]

What comes next in each series? Select one letter each time and mark it on the answer sheet.
Look at this example.

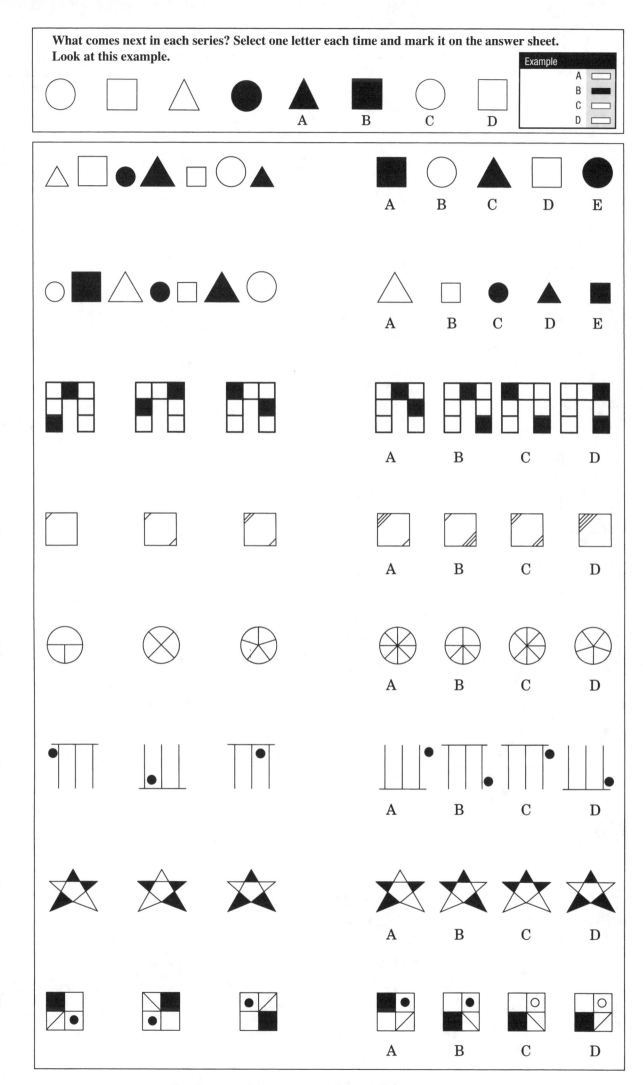

TEST 09 PAGE 4 – MULTIPLE CHOICE

In these questions the two shapes are either added together or subtracted from each other. The shapes do not turn. Select one answer each time and mark it on the answer sheet.

Example

A ☐
B ■
C ☐
D ☐

39

A   B   C   D

40

A   B   C   D

41

A   B   C   D

42

A   B   C   D

43

A   B   C   D

44

A   B   C   D

45

A   B   C   D

46

A   B   C   D

47

A   B   C   D

48

A   B   C   D

TEST 9 PAGE 5 – MULTIPLE CHOICE

Which shape is different from the other four?
Select one letter each time and mark it on the answer sheet.

Look at this example.

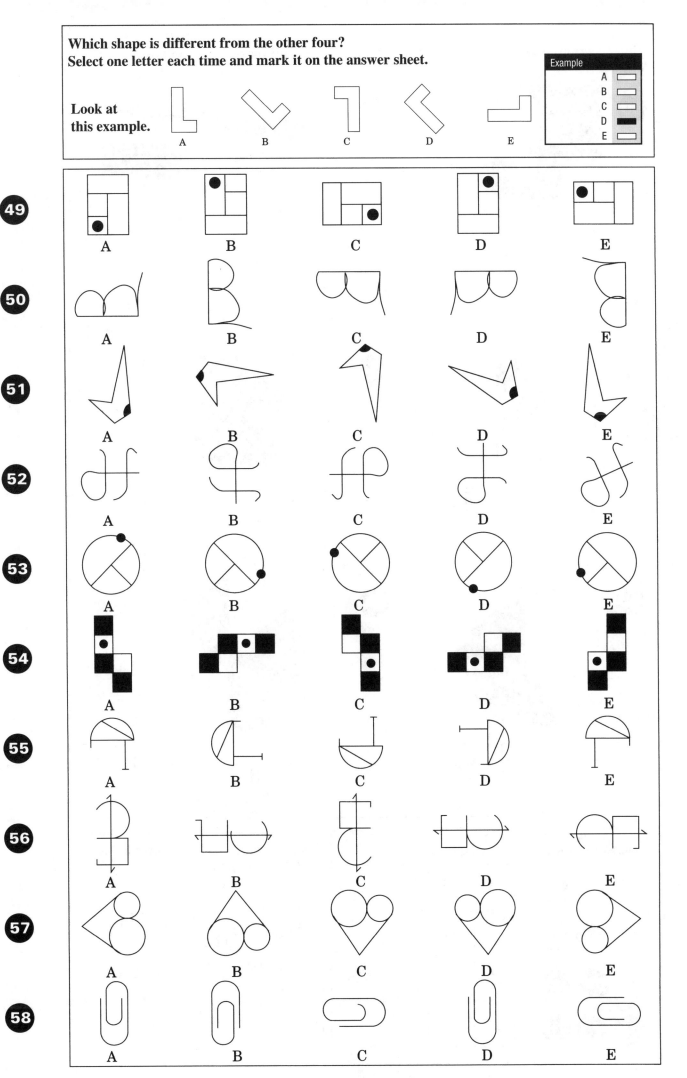

What fraction is shaded each time? Select one answer and mark it on the answer sheet.

59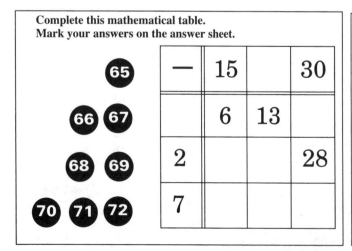

$\frac{3}{5}$ $\frac{2}{3}$ $\frac{1}{4}$ $\frac{5}{9}$

60

$\frac{1}{2}$ $\frac{1}{3}$ $\frac{2}{5}$ $\frac{1}{4}$

61

$\frac{1}{4}$ $\frac{1}{3}$ $\frac{3}{8}$ $\frac{2}{5}$

62

$\frac{2}{3}$ $\frac{3}{4}$ $\frac{5}{6}$ $\frac{4}{5}$

63

$\frac{3}{5}$ $\frac{2}{3}$ $\frac{3}{4}$ $\frac{7}{10}$

64

$\frac{2}{3}$ $\frac{1}{3}$ $\frac{5}{8}$ $\frac{2}{5}$

Complete this mathematical table.
Mark your answers on the answer sheet.

65

66 67

68 69

70 71 72

—	15		30
	6	13	
2			28
7			

Supply the missing numbers in this division sum. Mark your answers on the answer sheet.

73 74 $8\,\big|\,\Box\;2\;\Box$

75 $\quad\quad 1\;\Box\;5$

Rem 4

Preparation for 11+ and 12+ tests
Non Verbal Reasoning Book 2
Multiple Choice   ISBN 1-873385-31-7

Test 10

Pupils Name

Test Date

Example
A ☐
B ▬
C ☐
D ☐

1
A ☐
B ☐
C ☐
D ☐
E ☐

2
A ☐
B ☐
C ☐
D ☐
E ☐

3
A ☐
B ☐
C ☐
D ☐
E ☐

4
A ☐
B ☐
C ☐
D ☐
E ☐

5
A ☐
B ☐
C ☐
D ☐

6
A ☐
B ☐
C ☐
D ☐

7
A ☐
B ☐
C ☐
D ☐

8
A ☐
B ☐
C ☐
D ☐
E ☐

9
A ☐
B ☐
C ☐
D ☐
E ☐

10
A ☐
B ☐
C ☐
D ☐
E ☐

Example
A ☐
B ☐
C ☐
D ▬

11
A ☐
B ☐
C ☐
D ☐

12
A ☐
B ☐
C ☐
D ☐

13
A ☐
B ☐
C ☐
D ☐

14
A ☐
B ☐
C ☐
D ☐

15
A ☐
B ☐
C ☐
D ☐

16
A ☐
B ☐
C ☐
D ☐

17
A ☐
B ☐
C ☐
D ☐

18
A ☐
B ☐
C ☐
D ☐

19
A ☐
B ☐
C ☐
D ☐

20
A ☐
B ☐
C ☐
D ☐

21
A ☐
B ☐
C ☐
D ☐

22
A ☐
B ☐
C ☐
D ☐

23
A ☐
B ☐
C ☐
D ☐

24
A ☐
B ☐
C ☐
D ☐

25
A ☐
B ☐
C ☐
D ☐

26
A ☐
B ☐
C ☐
D ☐

27
A ☐
B ☐
C ☐
D ☐

28
A ☐
B ☐
C ☐
D ☐

29
A ☐
B ☐
C ☐
D ☐

30
A ☐
B ☐
C ☐
D ☐

Example
A ☐
B ☐
C ▬
D ☐

31
A ☐
B ☐
C ☐
D ☐

32
A ☐
B ☐
C ☐
D ☐

33
A ☐
B ☐
C ☐
D ☐

34
A ☐
B ☐
C ☐
D ☐

35
A ☐
B ☐
C ☐
D ☐

36
A ☐
B ☐
C ☐
D ☐

Please Turn Over

Please mark boxes with a single line ━ Do not mark outside the boxes

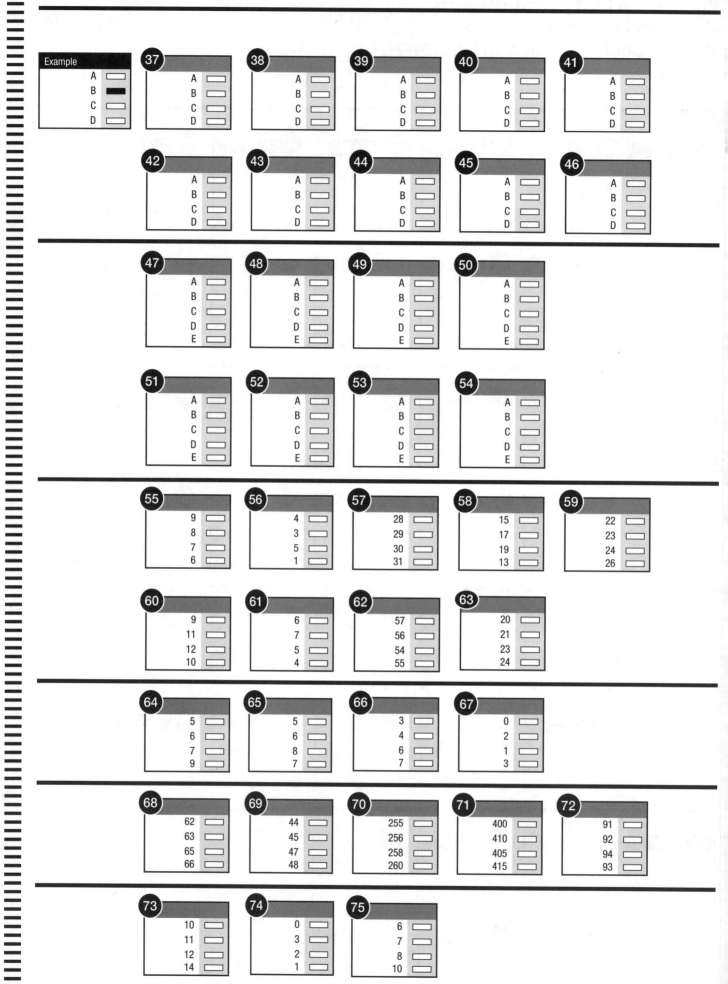

TEST 10

SCORE _____

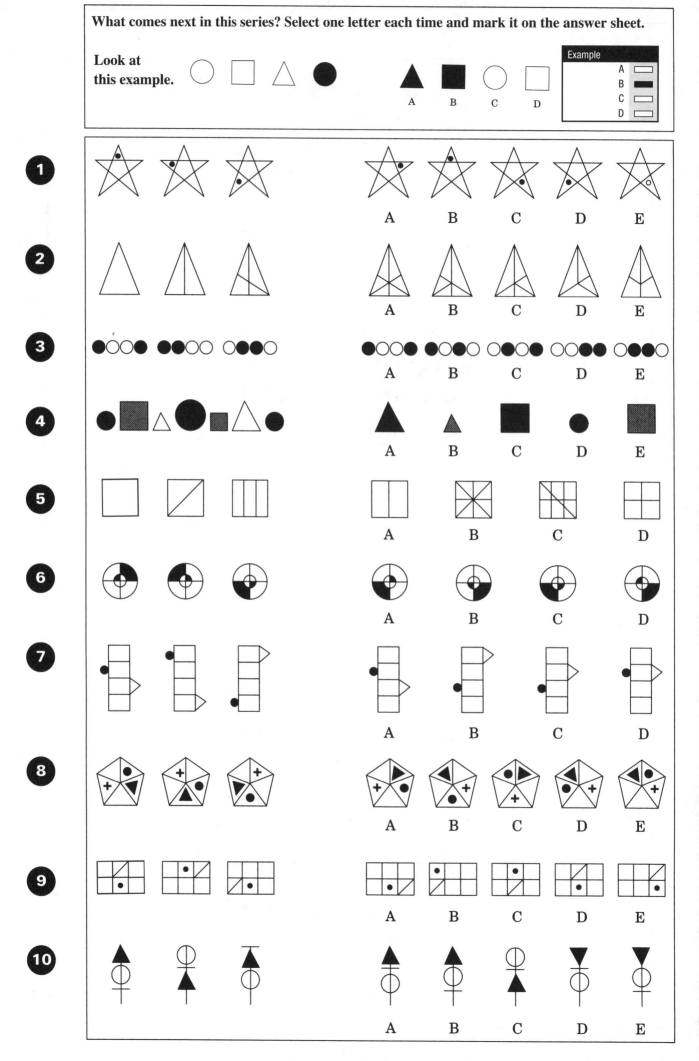

TEST 10 PAGE 1 – MULTIPLE CHOICE

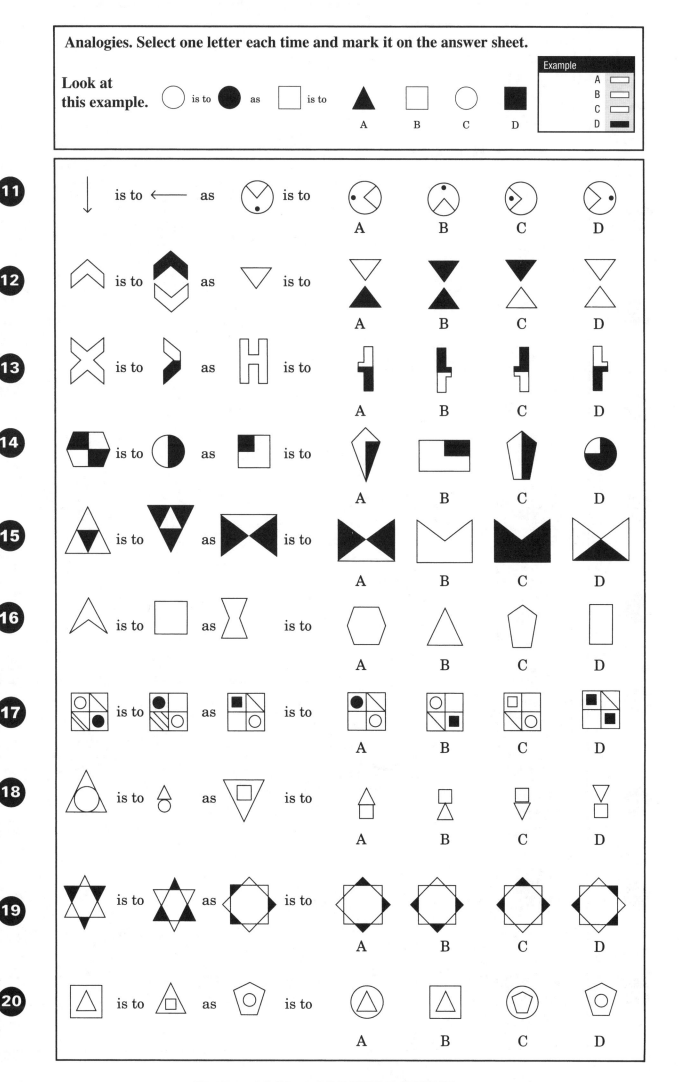

TEST 10 PAGE 2 – MULTIPLE CHOICE

Without turning the pieces over choose which piece completes the white jig-saw. Select one letter each time and mark it on the answer sheet.

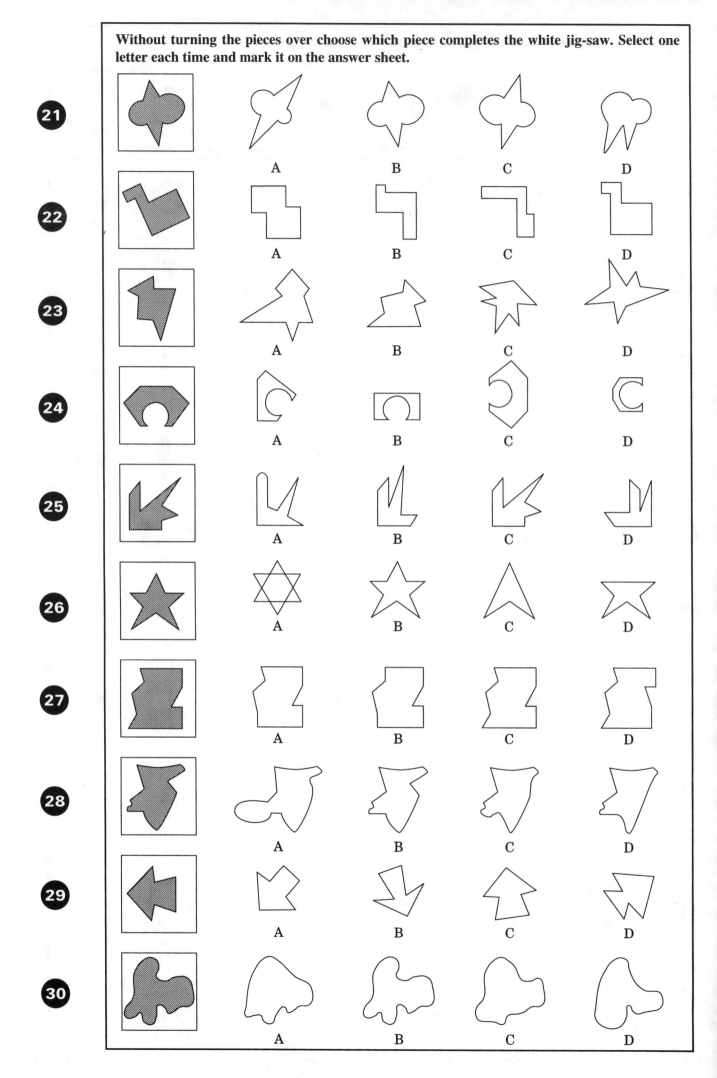

21   A   B   C   D

22   A   B   C   D

23   A   B   C   D

24   A   B   C   D

25   A   B   C   D

26   A   B   C   D

27   A   B   C   D

28   A   B   C   D

29   A   B   C   D

30   A   B   C   D

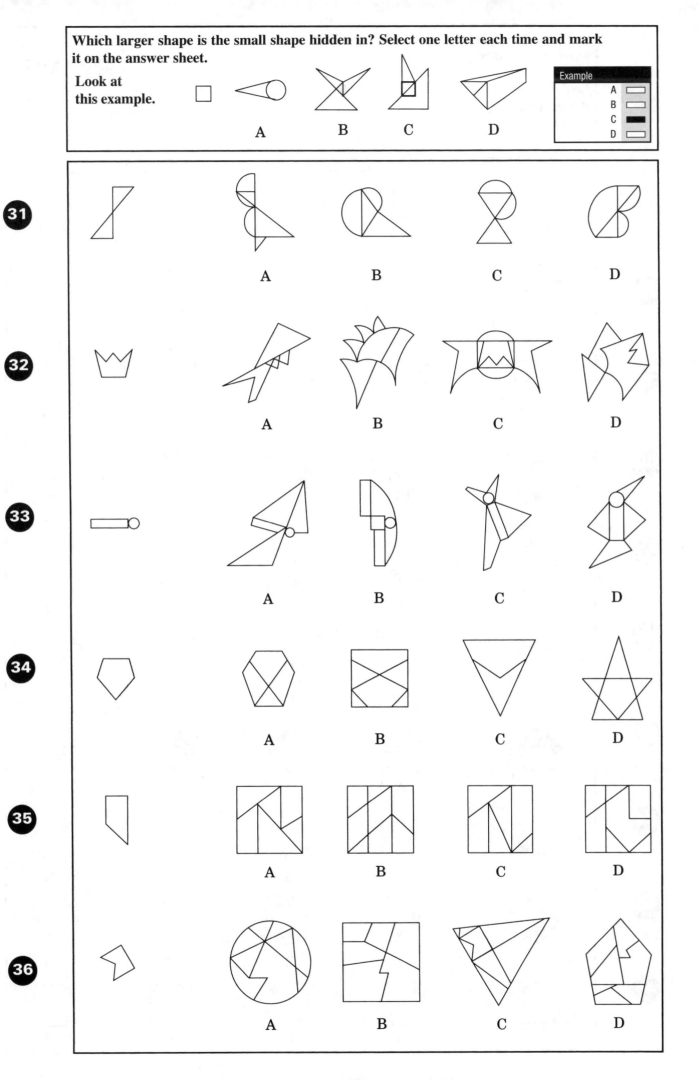

Which larger shape is the small shape hidden in? Select one letter each time and mark it on the answer sheet.

Look at this example.

A   B   C   D

Example

31

32

33

34

35

36

TEST 10 PAGE 4 – MULTIPLE CHOICE

Which shape has been rotated by ½ a turn? Select one letter each time and mark it on the answer sheet.

Look at this example.

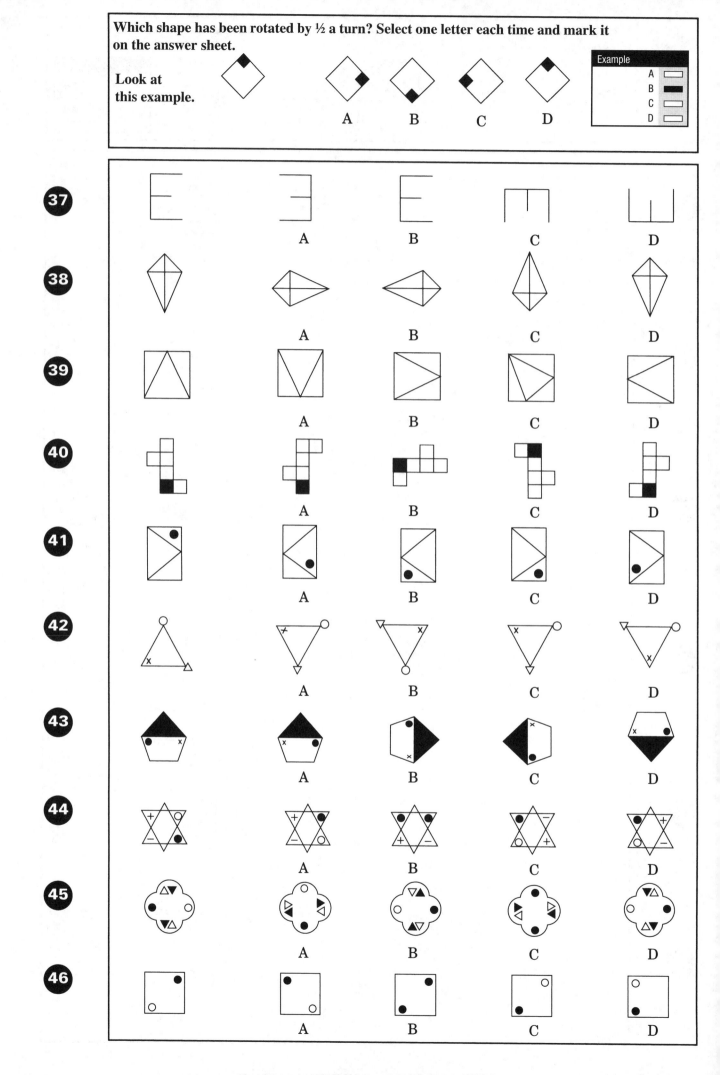

Which shape does not have a horizontal or a vertical line of symmetry?
Select one letter each time and mark it on the answer sheet.

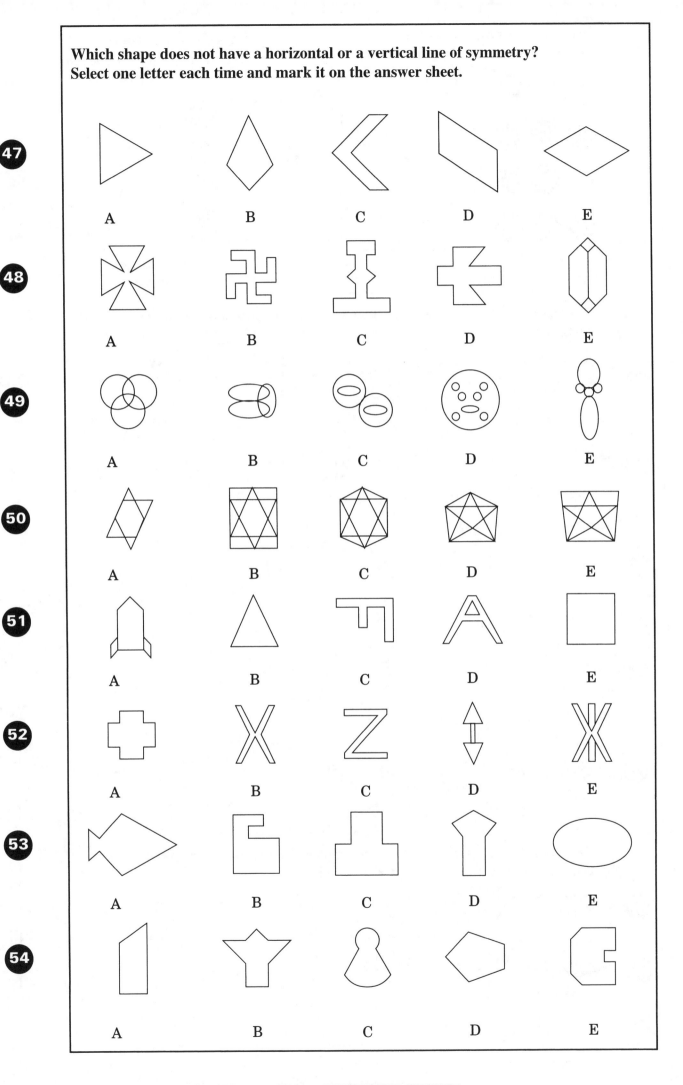

47

A   B   C   D   E

48

A   B   C   D   E

49

A   B   C   D   E

50

A   B   C   D   E

51

A   B   C   D   E

52

A   B   C   D   E

53

A   B   C   D   E

54

A   B   C   D   E

Complete this multiplication table.
Mark your answers on the answer sheet.

X	6		3
		40	
4		32	
	42		

Supply the missing numbers in this addition sum. Mark your answers on the answer sheet.

(64) 9 ☐ 5
(65) ☐ 5 8
(66) + 2 4 ☐
(67) ☐ 8 7 6

Find the number that continues each sequence in the correct way and mark it on the answer sheet.

(68) 8,   15,   24,   35,   48   [?]

(69) 2,   11,   16,   25,   30,   39   [?]

(70) 1,   4,   16,   64   [?]

(71) 5,   15,   45,   135   [?]

(72) 104,   20,   100,   24,   96,   28   [?]

Given that 36 ×12 = 432 complete the equation by finding the missing number that goes in the bracket. Mark your answer on the answer sheet.

(73) $432 \div 36 = (\underline{\quad ? \quad})$

(74) $432 \div 12 = 38 - (\underline{\quad ? \quad})$

(75) $432 \div 36 = 5 + (\underline{\quad ? \quad})$

ANSWER TO TEST 07

#	Answer	#	Answer
1.	B and D	39.	B
2.	C and E	40.	D
3.	B and E	41.	C
4.	A and D	42.	E
5.	C and E	43.	E
6.	A and E	44.	C
7.	B and D	45.	B
8.	A and E	46.	D
9.	C	47.	A
10.	B	48.	C
11.	A	49.	C
12.	C	50.	D
13.	D	51.	D
14.	A	52.	C
15.	D	53.	B
16.	B	54.	B
17.	C	55.	C
18.	C	56.	D
19.	C	57.	$3/4$
20.	D	58.	$3/8$
21.	A	59.	$3/4$
22.	E	60.	$1/2$
23.	D	61.	39
24.	B	62.	4
25.	C	63.	1
26.	C	64.	36
27.	D	65.	224
28.	A	66.	13
29.	D	67.	14
30.	B	68.	4
31.	C	69.	3
32.	C	70.	11
33.	B	71.	10
34.	A	72.	1
35.	F	73.	5
36.	E	74.	3
37.	A	75.	3
38.	C		

ANSWER TO TEST 06

#	Answer	#	Answer
1.	C and E	39.	B
2.	A and E	40.	E
3.	A and E	41.	B
4.	C and E	42.	D
5.	C and D	43.	C
6.	B and E	44.	A
7.	32 A + B + C	45.	E
8.	65 (A x B) + C	46.	A
9.	21 (A + B) - C	47.	C
10.	45 (A x B) + C	48.	D
11.	54 (A x B) - C	49.	1275
12.	10 A + B + C	50.	- 7.5
13.	C	51.	11
14.	D	52.	1.75
15.	A	53.	1.15
16.	D	54.	0.75
17.	D	55.	5
18.	B	56.	- 0.25
19.	48	57.	$1/3$
20.	1000	58.	$2/5$
21.	7.6	59.	$1/7$
22.	65	60.	$1/3$
23.	202.5	61.	$1/3$
24.	47	62.	$1/4$
25.	C	63.	12
26.	B	64.	1
27.	B	65.	2
28.	B	66.	6
29.	B	67.	3
30.	C	68.	4
31.	C	69.	6
32.	D	70.	5
33.	A	71.	1
34.	C	72.	1
35.	B	73.	7
36.	45 (3 x)	74.	4
37.	41 ($1/2$ x)	75.	1
38.	30 (x ÷ 4)		

A child who has not previously attempted questions of this type may have difficulty with the first few tests. However, it is generally accepted, that a child's ability to handle and understand these questions increases with practice.

www.learningtogether.co.uk   E-mail: info@learningtogether.co.uk
Learning Together: 18 Shandon Park, Belfast BT5 6NW   Phone/Fax: 028 9040 2086

ANSWERS TO TEST 08

#	Ans	#	Ans
1.	D	39.	A
2.	A	40.	C
3.	B	41.	B
4.	D	42.	D
5.	E	43.	C
6.	F	44.	E
7.	D	45.	B
8.	E	46.	21
9.	12	47.	1.26
10.	64	48.	-0.35
11.	24	49.	B
12.	C	50.	C
13.	B	51.	B
14.	D	52.	B
15.	C	53.	C
16.	D	54.	10
17.	C	55.	6
18.	B	56.	8
19.	B	57.	8
20.	B	58.	4
21.	D	59.	7
22.	C	60.	36
23.	B	61.	24
24.	C	62.	6
25.	C	63.	4
26.	C	64.	2
27.	A	65.	6
28.	C and E	66.	12
29.	B and E	67.	12
30.	B and D	68.	9
31.	C and D	69.	7
32.	B and F	70.	5
33.	C and F	71.	9
34.	128	72.	5
35.	85	73.	7
36.	5	74.	0
37.	72	75.	1
38.	F		

ANSWERS TO TEST 09

#	Ans	#	Ans
1.	C	39.	C
2.	A	40.	B
3.	D	41.	D
4.	B	42.	A
5.	C	43.	B
6.	A	44.	C
7.	D	45.	D
8.	C	46.	C
9.	C	47.	D
10.	B	48.	B
11.	A	49.	B
12.	B	50.	C
13.	E	51.	A
14.	E	52.	D
15.	C	53.	E
16.	D	54.	E
17.	D	55.	A
18.	A	56.	B
19.	9	57.	C
20.	10	58.	C
21.	10	59.	2/3
22.	11	60.	1/2
23.	11	61.	3/8
24.	11	62.	3/4
25.	47	63.	3/5
26.	21	64.	5/8
27.	27	65.	22
28.	6.4	66.	9
29.	23	67.	21
30.	9	68.	13
31.	A	69.	20
32.	E	70.	8
33.	B	71.	15
34.	C	72.	23
35.	D	73.	9
36.	D	74.	4
37.	A	75.	1
38.	B		

ANSWERS TO TEST 10

#	Ans	#	Ans
1.	C	39.	A
2.	A	40.	C
3.	D	41.	B
4.	E	42.	B
5.	D	43.	D
6.	B	44.	C
7.	C	45.	B
8.	C	46.	C
9.	C	47.	D
10.	B	48.	B
11.	A	49.	C
12.	C	50.	A
13.	D	51.	C
14.	B	52.	C
15.	D	53.	B
16.	A	54.	A
17.	B	55.	8
18.	D	56.	5
19.	D	57.	30
20.	C	58.	15
21.	B	59.	24
22.	D	60.	12
23.	B	61.	7
24.	C	62.	56
25.	C	63.	21
26.	B	64.	7
27.	C	65.	6
28.	B	66.	3
29.	C	67.	1
30.	B	68.	63
31.	D	69.	44
32.	C	70.	256
33.	C	71.	405
34.	D	72.	92
35.	B	73.	12
36.	C	74.	2
37.	A	75.	7
38.	C		